Childcraft

The How and Why Library

Volume 3

Stories and Poems

World Book, Inc.
a Scott Fetzer company

Chicago London Sydney Toronto

Acknowledgments

The publishers of *Childcraft—The How and Why Library*
gratefully acknowledge the courtesy of the following
publishers, agents, authors, and artists who have granted
permission to use copyrighted material in this book. Any
errors or omissions are unintentional and the publisher will be
happy to make any necessary corrections in future printings.
Full illustration acknowledgments for this volume appear on
page 300.

Allyn and Bacon, Inc.: "Do You Fear the Wind?" from *Prairie
Song and Western Story* by Hamlin Garland. Copyright ©
1928 by Allyn and Bacon, Inc. Reprinted with permission.
Angus and Robertson, Publishers: "Why the Kangaroo Hops
on Two Legs," an adaptation of the story "Bohra the
Kangaroo" from *Australian Legendary Tales* by K. Langloh
Parker, selected by H. Drake-Brockman. All rights
reserved. Reprinted by permission of Angus and
Robertson, Publishers.
Richard Armour: "Good Sportsmanship" from *Night with
Armour* by Richard Armour. Published by McGraw-Hill Inc.
Atheneum Publishers, Inc.: "The Nineteenth-Moon-of-Neptune
Beasts" from *The Phantom Ice Cream Man* by X. J.
Kennedy. Copyright © 1979 by X. J. Kennedy. (A
Margaret K. McElderry Book.) Reprinted with the
permission of Atheneum Publishers, Inc., and Curtis Brown,
Ltd. "To Dark Eyes Dreaming" from *Today Is Saturday* by
Zilpha Keatley Snyder. Text copyright © 1969 by Zilpha
Keatley Snyder. Reprinted with the permission of Atheneum
Publishers, Inc.
Patricia Ayers: "Associations" from *There Is No Rhyme for
Silver* by Eve Merriam. Copyright © 1962 by Eve Merriam.
Reprinted by permission of the author.
Branden Press: "Wild Geese" from *The City and Other
Poems* by Elinor Chipp. Copyright 1923 by The Four Seas
Co. Reprinted courtesy of Branden Press, 21 Station
Street, Brookline Village, MA 02147.
Mary E. Cober: "How It Snowed Fur and Rained Fry Cakes in
Western Virginia" from *The Remarkable History of Tony
Beaver, West Virginian* by Mary E. Cober. Copyright ©
1981.
William Cole: "Banananananananananana" by William Cole.
Copyright © 1977 by William Cole. "Back Yard, July
Night" from *A Boy Named Mary Jane and Other Silly Verse*
by William Cole. Copyright © 1969, 1977 by William Cole.
Harold Courlander: "The Cow-Tail Switch" from *The Cow-Tail
Switch and Other West African Stories* by Harold
Courlander and George Herzog. Copyright © 1947 by Holt,
Rinehart and Winston. Copyright © 1975 by Harold
Courlander and George Herzog.
The Curtis Publishing Company: "Far Trek" by June Brady.
Reprinted from *The Saturday Evening Post* © 1974 The
Curtis Publishing Company.
Dodd, Mead & Company: "Glooscap and His People" from
Glooscap and His Magic: Legends of the Wabanaki Indians
by Kay Hill. Copyright © 1963 by Kay Hill. Reprinted by
permission of Dodd, Mead & Company, Inc., the Canadian
Publishers, McClelland and Stewart Limited, Toronto, and
Victor Gollancz, Ltd., London.
Doubleday & Company, Inc.: "The Road Back" by Chora and
"The Firefly Hunt" by Ryusui from *An Introduction to Haiku*
by Harold G. Henderson. Copyright © 1958 by Harold G.
Henderson. Reprinted by permission of Doubleday &
Company, Inc.
E. P. Dutton, Inc.: "The Flight of Icarus" and "Theseus and
the Minotaur" from *Stories of the Gods and Heroes.*
Copyright 1940, renewed 1968 by Sally Benson. Reprinted
by permission of the publisher, Dial Books for Young
Readers, a Division of E. P. Dutton, Inc.

Grosset & Dunlap, Inc., Publishers: "Football" by Walt
Mason. Reprinted by permission of Grosset & Dunlap from
Walt Mason, His Book by Walt Mason. Copyright 1916 by
Barse & Hopkins.
Harcourt Brace Jovanovich, Inc.: "A mountain village," "How
cool cut hay smells," "I must go begging," "In spring the
chirping," "What a wonderful," and "When my canary"
from *Cricket Songs: Japanese Haiku,* translated and
copyright © 1964 by Harry Behn. Reprinted by permission
of Harcourt Brace Jovanovich, Inc., and Curtis Brown, Ltd.
"Others" from *The Wizard in the Well* by Harry Behn.
Copyright © 1956 by Harry Behn. Reprinted by permission
of Harcourt Brace Jovanovich, Inc. "Macavity: The Mystery
Cat" from *Old Possum's Book of Practical Cats.* Copyright
1939 by T. S. Eliot; renewed 1967 by Esme Valerie Eliot.
Reprinted by permission of Harcourt Brace Jovanovich,
Inc., and Faber and Faber Ltd. Illustration copyright ©
1982 by Edward Gorey. Reproduced by permission of
Harcourt Brace Jovanovich, Inc. "Clever Manka."
Copyright 1920 by Parker Fillmore; renewed 1948 by
Louise Fillmore. Reprinted from *The Shepherd's Nosegay*
by permission of Harcourt Brace Jovanovich, Inc. "Fog"
from *Chicago Poems* by Carl Sandburg. Copyright 1916 by
Holt, Rinehart, and Winston, Inc.; renewed 1944 by Carl
Sandburg. Reprinted by permission of Harcourt Brace
Jovanovich, Inc.
Harper & Row, Publishers, Inc.: "The Homecoming"
excerpted from *Sounder* by William H. Armstrong. Text
copyright © 1969 by William H. Armstrong. Reprinted by
permission of Harper & Row, Publishers, Inc., and Victor
Gollancz Ltd. "Harriet's Secret" excerpted from *Harriet the
Spy* by Louise Fitzhugh. Copyright © 1964 by Louise
Fitzhugh. Reprinted by permission of Harper & Row,
Publishers, Inc., and Victor Gollancz Ltd., London. "Nina
Terrance," Chapter 2 from *The Cry of the Crow* by Jean
Craighead George. Copyright © 1980 by Jean Craighead
George. Reprinted by permission of Harper & Row,
Publishers, Inc., and Curtis Brown, Ltd. "A Bug Sat in a
Silver Flower" from *Dogs and Dragons, Trees and Dreams*
by Karla Kuskin. Copyright © 1980 by Karla Kuskin.
"Anansi and the Plantains" from *Anansi the Spider Man:
Jamaican Folk Tales* told by Philip M. Sherlock (Thomas Y.
Crowell). Copyright 1954 by Philip M. Sherlock. Reprinted
by permission of Harper & Row, Publishers, Inc., and
Macmillan Publishers Ltd., London and Basingstoke. "The
Challenge" excerpted from *Sea Glass* by Laurence Yep.
Copyright © 1979 by Laurence Yep. Reprinted by
permission of Harper & Row, Publishers, Inc., and The
Sterling Lord Agency, Inc.
Holiday House: "Thunder Butte" reprinted from *When
Thunder Spoke* by Virginia Driving Hawk Sneve. Copyright
© 1974 by Virginia Driving Hawk Sneve. Used by
permission of Holiday House.
Houghton Mifflin Company: "The Living Kuan-Yin" from
Sweet and Sour: Tales from China retold by Carol Kendall
and Yao-wen Li. Copyright © 1980 by Carol Kendall and
Yao-wen Li. Reprinted by permission of Ticknor &
Fields/Clarion Books, a Houghton Mifflin Company, and
The Bodley Head. "The Boy Who Became a Wizard" from
A Wizard of Earthsea by Ursula K. Le Guin. Copyright ©
1968 by Ursula K. LeGuin for story. Reprinted by
permission of Houghton Mifflin Company. "I Leave the
Island" (pages 59–70) from *Island of the Blue Dolphins* by
Scott O'Dell. Copyright © 1960 by Scott O'Dell. Reprinted
by permission of Houghton Mifflin Company, and Penguin
Books Ltd. "A Stranger in a Land" from *The Witch of
Blackbird Pond* by Elizabeth George Speare. Copyright ©
1958 by Elizabeth George Speare. Reprinted by permission
of Houghton Mifflin Company, and Victor Gollancz Ltd. "A
New Way" from *Toolmaker* by Jill Paton Walsh. Copyright
© 1973 by Jill Paton Walsh. Reprinted by permission of
Ticknor & Fields/Clarion Books, A Houghton Mifflin
Company, and William Heinemann Limited.
Indiana University Press: "Baba Yaga's Geese" from *Baba
Yaga's Geese and Other Russian Stories,* translated and
adapted by Bonnie Carey.
Ray Lincoln Literary Agency: "The Hound" from *Don't Ever
Cross a Crocodile and Other Poems* by Kaye Starbird.
Copyright © 1963 by Kaye Starbird. Reprinted by
permission of Ray Lincoln Literary Agency, 4 Surrey Road,
Melrose Park, Pa. 19126.
Little, Brown and Company: "This Is My Rock" from *One at a
Time* by David McCord. Copyright © 1929 by David
McCord. First appeared in *Saturday Review.* By permission
of Little, Brown and Company. Also appeared in *Mr.
Bidery's Spidery Garden* published by Harrap Ltd. and
reprinted with their permission. "I Find Wol" from *Owls in
the Family* by Farley Mowat. Copyright © 1961 by Farley
Mowat. By permission of Little, Brown and Company in
association with the Atlantic Monthly Press, and the
Canadian Publishers, McClelland and Stewart Limited,
Toronto. "Eletelephony" from *Tirra Lirra: Rhymes Old and
New* by Laura E. Richards. Copyright © 1930, 1932 by
Laura E. Richards. Copyright © 1960 by Hamilton
Richards. By permission of Little, Brown and Company.
Macmillan Publishing Company: "Swift Things Are Beautiful"
from *Away Goes Sally* by Elizabeth Coatsworth. Copyright
1934 by Macmillan Publishing Co., Inc. Copyright renewed

(continued on page 300)

Volume 3

Stories and Poems

Contents

About This Book

When you were very young, you had some favorite things that you enjoyed day after day—a picture book, nursery rhymes, a fairy tale. When you learned to read, you found some books that were special, and your list of favorites grew. In *Stories and Poems*, you'll find some new favorites to add to your old ones—folk tales, fantasies, and real-life adventures, and poems that are thoughtful or magical or good for a giggle.

Stories and Poems contains 27 stories and 91 poems for you to enjoy. Here is your chance to go adventuring in many times and places: ancient Greece and China, colonial America, and modern-day California, Florida, and New York. You can raise an orphan crow or a baby owl, sail a pirate ship to safety, or weave an enchantment that saves a town.

You'll meet characters you will remember—bold Robin Hood, quietly brave Karana, and many more. And you'll discover that some of these characters face problems and predicaments that are very like your own. In "Harriet's Secret," Harriet's classmates read her private notebook—and find out what she has written about them. And in "The Challenge," Craig Chin struggles to win the respect of a new friend, who is a rather fearsome old man.

Folk tales are fun because they show how wise (and how foolish) people can be. Po Wan's generous heart leads him to lose a fortune—and then gain another one. Manka's cleverness wins a husband, loses him, and wins him back. And an emperor and his courtiers are so worried about what others think that they won't believe what their eyes tell them.

If you find a story you like, read the note at the end. It will tell you about other good stories you can find at the library—and about books on subjects that may interest you.

Don't forget the poems. Some of them are "picture" poems that lead you to see things in a fresh, new way. Some of them are "idea" poems that leave you with interesting things to think about. And quite a few are high nonsense and just plain fun.

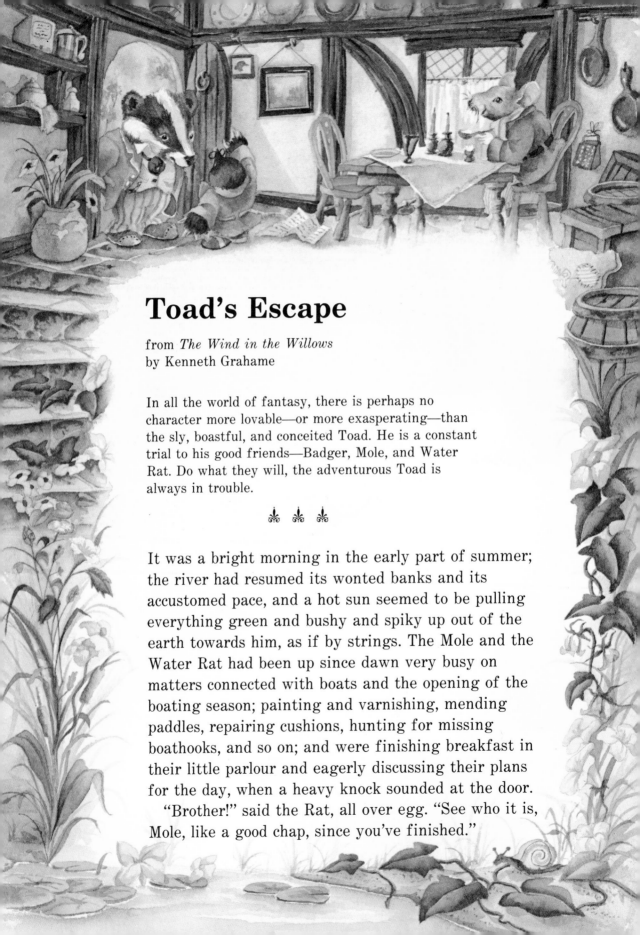

Toad's Escape

from *The Wind in the Willows*
by Kenneth Grahame

In all the world of fantasy, there is perhaps no character more lovable—or more exasperating—than the sly, boastful, and conceited Toad. He is a constant trial to his good friends—Badger, Mole, and Water Rat. Do what they will, the adventurous Toad is always in trouble.

⚜ ⚜ ⚜

It was a bright morning in the early part of summer; the river had resumed its wonted banks and its accustomed pace, and a hot sun seemed to be pulling everything green and bushy and spiky up out of the earth towards him, as if by strings. The Mole and the Water Rat had been up since dawn very busy on matters connected with boats and the opening of the boating season; painting and varnishing, mending paddles, repairing cushions, hunting for missing boathooks, and so on; and were finishing breakfast in their little parlour and eagerly discussing their plans for the day, when a heavy knock sounded at the door.

"Brother!" said the Rat, all over egg. "See who it is, Mole, like a good chap, since you've finished."

The Mole went to attend the summons, and the Rat heard him utter a cry of surprise. Then he flung the parlour door open, and announced with much importance, "Mr. Badger!"

This was a wonderful thing, indeed, that the Badger should pay a formal call on them, or indeed on anybody. He generally had to be caught, if you wanted him badly, as he slipped quietly along a hedgerow of an early morning or a late evening, or else hunted up in his own house in the middle of the wood, which was a serious undertaking.

The Badger strode heavily into the room, and stood looking at the two animals with an expression full of seriousness. The Rat let his egg-spoon fall on the tablecloth, and sat open-mouthed.

"The hour has come!" said the Badger at last with great solemnity.

"What hour?" asked the Rat uneasily, glancing at the clock on the mantelpiece.

"*Whose* hour, you should rather say," replied the Badger. "Why, Toad's hour! The hour of Toad! I said I would take him in hand as soon as the winter was well over, and I'm going to take him in hand today!"

"Toad's hour, of course!" cried the Mole delightedly. "Hooray! I remember now! *We'll* teach him to be a sensible Toad!"

"This very morning," continued the Badger, taking an armchair, "as I learnt last night from a trustworthy source, another new and exceptionally powerful motor-car will arrive at Toad Hall on approval or return. At this very moment, perhaps. Toad is busy arraying himself in those singularly hideous habiliments so dear to him, which transform him from a (comparatively) good-looking Toad into an Object which throws any decent-minded animal that comes across it into a violent fit. We must be up and doing, before it is too late. You two animals will accompany

me instantly to Toad Hall, and the work of rescue shall be accomplished."

"Right you are!" cried the Rat, starting up. "We'll rescue the poor unhappy animal! We'll convert him! He'll be the most converted Toad that ever was before we're done with him!"

They set off up the road on their mission of mercy, Badger leading the way. Animals when in company walk in a proper and sensible manner, in single file, instead of sprawling all across the road and being of no use or support to each other in case of sudden trouble or danger.

They reached the carriage-drive of Toad Hall to find, as the Badger had anticipated, a shiny new motor-car, of great size, painted a bright red (Toad's favourite colour), standing in front of the house. As they neared the door it was flung open, and Mr. Toad, arrayed in goggles, cap, gaiters, and enormous overcoat, came swaggering down the steps, drawing on his gauntleted gloves.

"Hullo! come on, you fellows!" he cried cheerfully on catching sight of them. "You're just in time to come with me for a jolly—to come for a jolly—for a—er—jolly——"

His hearty accents faltered and fell away as he noticed the stern unbending look on the countenances of his silent friends, and his invitation remained unfinished.

The Badger strode up the steps. "Take him inside," he said sternly to his companions. Then, as Toad was hustled through the door, struggling and protesting, he turned to the chauffeur in charge of the new motor-car.

"I'm afraid you won't be wanted today," he said. "Mr. Toad has changed his mind. He will not require the car. Please understand that this is final. You needn't wait." Then he followed the others inside and shut the door.

"Now, then!" he said to the Toad, when the four of them stood together in the hall, "first of all, take those ridiculous things off!"

"Shan't!" replied Toad, with great spirit. "What is the meaning of this gross outrage? I demand an instant explanation."

"Take them off him, then, you two," ordered the Badger briefly.

They had to lay Toad out on the floor, kicking and calling all sorts of names, before they could get to work properly. Then the Rat sat on him, and the Mole got his motor-clothes off him bit by bit, and they stood him up on his legs again. A good deal of his blustering spirit seemed to have evaporated with the removal of his fine panoply. Now that he was merely Toad, and no longer the Terror of the Highway, he giggled feebly and looked from one to the other appealingly, seeming quite to understand the situation.

"You knew it must come to this, sooner or later, Toad," the Badger explained severely. "You've disregarded all the warnings we've given you, you've gone on squandering the money your father left you, and you're getting us animals a bad name in the district by your furious driving and your smashes and your rows with the police. Independence is all very well, but we animals never allow our friends to make fools of themselves beyond a certain limit; and that limit you've reached. Now, you're a good fellow in many respects, and I don't want to be too hard on you. I'll make one more effort to bring you to reason. You will come with me into the smoking-room, and there you will hear some facts about yourself; and we'll see whether you come out of that room the same Toad that you went in."

He took Toad firmly by the arm, led him into the smoking-room and closed the door behind them.

"*That's* no good!" said the Rat contemptuously. "*Talking* to Toad'll never cure him. He'll *say* anything."

They made themselves comfortable in armchairs and waited patiently. Through the closed door they could just hear the long continuous drone of the Badger's voice, rising and falling in waves of oratory; and presently they noticed that the sermon began to be punctuated at intervals by long-drawn sobs, evidently proceeding from the bosom of Toad, who was a soft-hearted and affectionate fellow, very easily converted—for the time being—to any point of view.

After some three-quarters of an hour the door opened, and the Badger reappeared, solemnly leading by the paw a very limp and dejected Toad. His skin hung baggily about him, his legs wobbled, and his cheeks were furrowed by the tears so plentifully called forth by the Badger's moving discourse.

"Sit down there, Toad," said the Badger kindly, pointing to a chair. "My friends," he went on, "I am pleased to inform you that Toad has at last seen the error of his ways. He is truly sorry for his misguided conduct in the past, and he has undertaken to give up motor-cars entirely and forever. I have his solemn promise to that effect."

"That is very good news," said the Mole gravely.

"Very good news indeed," observed the Rat dubiously, "if only—*if* only—"

He was looking very hard at Toad as he said this, and could not help thinking he perceived something vaguely resembling a twinkle in that animal's sorrowful eye.

"There's only one thing more to be done," continued the gratified Badger. "Toad, I want you solemnly to repeat, before your friends here, what you fully admitted to me in the smoking-room just now. First, you are sorry for what you've done, and you see the folly of it all?"

There was a long, long pause. Toad looked desperately this way and that, while the other animals waited in grave silence. At last he spoke.

"No!" he said a little sullenly, but stoutly. "I'm *not* sorry. And it wasn't folly at all! It was simply glorious!"

"What?" cried the Badger, greatly scandalized. "You backsliding animal, didn't you tell me just now, in there——"

"O, yes, yes, in *there*," said Toad impatiently. "I'd have said anything in *there*. You're so eloquent, dear Badger, and so moving, and so convincing, and put all your points so frightfully well—you can do what you like with me in *there*, and you know it. But I've been searching my mind since, and going over things in it, and I find that I'm not a bit sorry or repentant really, so it's no earthly good saying I am; now, is it?"

"Then you don't promise," said the Badger, "never to touch a motor-car again?"

"Certainly not!" replied Toad emphatically. "On the contrary, I faithfully promise that the very first motor-car I see, poop-poop! off I go in it!"

"Told you so, didn't I?" observed the Rat to the Mole.

"Very well, then," said the Badger firmly, rising to his feet. "Since you won't yield to persuasion, we'll try what force can do. I feared it would come to this all along. You've often asked us three to come and stay with you, Toad, in this handsome house of yours; well, now we're going to. When we've converted you to take a proper point of view we may quit, but not before. Take him upstairs, you two, and lock him up in his bedroom, while we arrange matters between ourselves."

"It's for your own good, Toady, you know," said the Rat kindly, as Toad, kicking and struggling, was hauled up the stairs by his two faithful friends. "Think what fun we shall all have together, just as we used to, when you've quite got over this—this painful attack of yours!"

"We'll take great care of everything for you till you're well, Toad," said the Mole; "and we'll see your money isn't wasted, as it has been."

"No more of those regrettable incidents with the police, Toad," said the Rat, as they thrust him into his bedroom.

"And no more weeks in hospital, being ordered about by female nurses, Toad," added the Mole, turning the key on him.

They descended the stair, Toad shouting abuse at them through the keyhole; and the three friends then met in conference on the situation.

"It's going to be a tedious business," said the Badger, sighing. "I've never seen Toad so determined. However, we will see it out. He must never be left an instant unguarded. We shall have to take it in turns to be with him, till the poison has worked itself out of his system."

They arranged watches accordingly. Each animal took it in turns to sleep in Toad's room at night, and they divided the day up between them. At first Toad was undoubtedly very trying to his careful guardians. When his violent paroxysms possessed him he would arrange bedroom chairs in rude resemblance of a motor-car and would crouch on the foremost of them, bent forward and staring fixedly ahead, making uncouth and ghastly noises, till the climax was reached, when, turning a complete somersault, he would lie prostrate amidst the ruins of the chairs, apparently completely satisfied for the moment. As time passed, however, these painful seizures grew gradually less frequent, and his friends strove to divert his mind into fresh channels. But his interest in other matters did not seem to revive, and he grew apparently languid and depressed.

One fine morning the Rat, whose turn it was to go on duty, went upstairs to relieve Badger, whom he found fidgeting to be off and stretch his legs in a long ramble round his wood and down his earths and burrows. "Toad's still in bed," he told the Rat, outside the door. "Can't get much out of him, except, O, leave him alone, he wants nothing, perhaps he'll be better presently, it may pass off in time, don't be unduly anxious, and so on. Now, you look out, Rat! When Toad's quiet and submissive, and playing at being the hero of a Sunday-school prize, then he's at his artfullest. There's sure to be something up. I know him. Well, now I must be off."

"How are you today, old chap?" inquired the Rat cheerfully, as he approached Toad's bedside.

He had to wait some minutes for an answer. At last a feeble voice replied, "Thank you so much, dear Ratty! So good of you to inquire! But first tell me how you are yourself, and the excellent Mole?"

"O, *we're* all right," replied the Rat. "Mole," he added incautiously, "is getting out for a run round with Badger. They'll be out till luncheon-time, so you and I will spend a pleasant morning together, and I'll do my best to amuse you. Now jump up, there's a good fellow, and don't lie moping there on a fine morning like this!"

"Dear, kind Rat," murmured Toad, "how little you

realize my condition, and how very far I am from 'jumping up' now—if ever! But do not trouble about me. I hate being a burden to my friends, and I do not expect to be one much longer. Indeed, I almost hope not."

"Well, I hope not, too," said the Rat heartily. "You've been a fine bother to us all this time, and I'm glad to hear it's going to stop. And in weather like this, and the boating season just beginning! It's too bad of you, Toad! It isn't the trouble we mind, but you're making us miss such an awful lot."

"I'm afraid it *is* the trouble you mind, though," replied the Toad languidly. "I can quite understand it. It's natural enough. You're tired of bothering about me. I mustn't ask you to do anything further. I'm a nuisance, I know."

"You are, indeed," said the Rat. "But I tell you, I'd take any trouble on earth for you, if only you'd be a sensible animal."

"If I thought that, Ratty," murmured Toad, more feebly than ever, "then I would beg you—for the last time, probably—to step around to the village as quickly as possible—even now it may be too late—and fetch

the doctor. But don't you bother. It's only a trouble, and perhaps we may as well let things take their course."

"Why, what do you want a doctor for?" inquired the Rat, coming closer and examining him. He certainly lay very still and flat, and his voice was weaker and his manner much changed.

"Surely you have noticed of late—" murmured Toad. "But no—why should you? Noticing things is only a trouble. Tomorrow, indeed, you may be saying to yourself, 'Oh, if only I had noticed sooner! If only I had done something!' But no; it's a trouble. Never mind—forget that I asked."

"Look here, old man," said the Rat, beginning to get rather alarmed, "of course I'll fetch a doctor for you, if you really think you want him. But you can hardly be bad enough for that yet. Let's talk about something else."

"I fear, dear friend," said Toad, with a sad smile, "that 'talk' can do little in a case like this—or doctors either, for that matter; still, one must grasp at the slightest straw. And, by the way—while you are about it—I *hate* to give you additional trouble, but I happen to remember that you will pass the door—would you mind at the same time asking the lawyer to step up? It would be a convenience to me, and there are moments—perhaps I should say there is *a* moment—when one must face disagreeable tasks, at whatever cost to exhausted nature!"

"A lawyer! O, he must be really bad!" the affrighted Rat said to himself, as he hurried from the room, not forgetting, however, to lock the door carefully behind him.

Outside, he stopped to consider. The other two were far away, and he had no one to consult.

"It's best to be on the safe side," he said, on reflection. "I've known Toad fancy himself frightfully

bad before, without the slightest reason; but I've never heard him ask for a lawyer! If there's nothing really the matter, the doctor will tell him he's an old fool, and cheer him up; and that will be something gained. I'd better humour him and go; it won't take very long." So he ran off to the village on his errand of mercy.

The Toad, who had hopped lightly out of bed as soon as he heard the key turned in the lock, watched him eagerly from the window till he disappeared down the carriage-drive. Then, laughing heartily, he dressed as quickly as possible in the smartest suit he could lay hands on at the moment, filled his pockets with cash which he took from a small drawer in the dressing-table, and next, knotting the sheets from his bed together and tying one end of the improvised rope round the central mullion of the handsome Tudor window which formed such a feature of his bedroom, he scrambled out, slid lightly to the ground, and, taking the opposite direction to the Rat, marched off light-heartedly, whistling a merry tune.

It was a gloomy luncheon for Rat when the Badger and the Mole at length returned, and he had to face them at table with his pitiful and unconvincing story. The Badger's caustic, not to say brutal, remarks may be imagined, and therefore passed over; but it was painful to the Rat that even the Mole, though he took his friend's side as far as possible, could not help saying, "You've been a bit of a duffer this time, Ratty! Toad, too, of all animals!"

"He did it awfully well," said the crestfallen Rat.

"He did *you* awfully well!" rejoined the Badger hotly. "However, talking won't mend matters. He's got clear away for the time, that's certain; and the worst of it is, he'll be so conceited with what he'll think is his cleverness that he may commit any folly. One comfort is, we're free now, and needn't waste any more of our precious time doing sentry-go. But we'd better continue to sleep at Toad Hall for a while longer. Toad may be brought back at any moment—on a stretcher, or between two policemen."

So spoke the Badger, not knowing what the future held in store, or how much water, and of how turbid a character, was to run under bridges before Toad should sit at ease again in his ancestral Hall.

Meanwhile, Toad, gay and irresponsible, was walking briskly along the high road, some miles from home. At first he had taken bypaths, and crossed many fields, and changed his course several times, in case of pursuit; but now, feeling by this time safe from recapture, and the sun smiling brightly on him, and all Nature joining in a chorus of approval to the song of self-praise that his own heart was singing to him, he almost danced along the road in his satisfaction and conceit.

"Smart piece of work that!" he remarked to himself, chuckling. "Brain against brute force—and brain came out on top—as it's bound to do. Poor old Ratty! My!

won't he catch it when the Badger gets back! A worthy fellow, Ratty, with many good qualities, but very little intelligence and absolutely no education. I must take him in hand some day, and see if I can make something of him."

Filled full of conceited thoughts such as these he strode along, his head in the air, till he reached a little town, where the sign of "The Red Lion," swinging across the road half-way down the main street, reminded him that he had not breakfasted that day, and that he was exceedingly hungry after his long walk. He marched into the inn, ordered the best luncheon that could be provided at so short a notice, and sat down to eat it in the coffee-room.

He was about half-way through his meal when an only too familiar sound, approaching down the street, made him start and fall a-trembling all over. The poop-poop! drew nearer and nearer, the car could be heard to turn into the inn-yard and come to a stop, and Toad had to hold on to the leg of the table to conceal his overmastering emotion. Presently the party entered the coffee-room, hungry, talkative, and gay, voluble on their experiences of the morning and the merits of the chariot that had brought them along so well. Toad listened eagerly, all ears, for a time; at last

he could stand it no longer. He slipped out of the room
quietly, paid his bill at the bar, and as soon as he got
outside sauntered round quietly to the inn-yard. "There
cannot be any harm," he said to himself, "in my only
just *looking* at it!"

The car stood in the middle of the yard, quite
unattended, the stable-helps and other hangers-on
being all at their dinner. Toad walked slowly round it,
inspecting, criticizing, musing deeply.

"I wonder," he said to himself presently, "I wonder
if this sort of car *starts* easily?"

Next moment, hardly knowing how it came about, he
found he had hold of the handle and was turning it. As
the familiar sound broke forth, the old passion seized
on Toad and completely mastered him, body and soul.
As if in a dream he found himself, somehow, seated in
the driver's seat; as if in a dream, he pulled the lever
and swung the car round the yard and out through the
archway; and, as if in a dream, all sense of right and
wrong, all fear of obvious consequences, seemed

temporarily suspended. He increased his pace, and as
the car devoured the street and leapt forth on the high
road through the open country, he was only conscious
that he was Toad once more, Toad at his best and
highest, Toad the terror, the traffic-queller, the Lord
of the lone trail, before whom all must give way or be
smitten into nothingness and everlasting night. He
chanted as he flew, and the car responded with
sonorous drone; the miles were eaten up under him as
he sped he knew not whither, fulfilling his instincts,
living his hour, reckless of what might come to him.

Will Badger, Mole, and Water Rat ever be able to save
the reckless Toad from himself? Read *The Wind in the
Willows*, the book from which this story came, and
find out for yourself. And while you are at it, try *The
Reluctant Dragon*, another of Kenneth Grahame's
fanciful tales. Also, if you turn the page, you'll find a
little song boastful Toad made up about himself.

Toad's Song

from *The Wind in the Willows*
by Kenneth Grahame

"The world has held great Heroes,
    As history-books have showed;
But never a name to go down to fame
    Compared with that of Toad!

"The clever men at Oxford[1]
    Know all that there is to be knowed.
But they none of them know one half as much
    As intelligent Mr. Toad!

"The animals sat in the Ark and cried,
    Their tears in torrents flowed.
Who was it said, 'There's land ahead?'
    Encouraging Mr. Toad!

"The army all saluted
    As they marched along the road.
Was it the King? Or Kitchener?[2]
    No. It was Mr. Toad!

"The Queen and her Ladies-in-waiting
    Sat at the window and sewed.
She cried, 'Look! who's that *handsome* man?'
    They answered, 'Mr. Toad.' "

Don't Worry if Your Job Is Small

author unknown

Don't worry if your job is small,
And your rewards are few.
Remember that the mighty oak,
Was once a nut like you.

---

1. Oxford is the oldest university in Great Britain.
2. Kitchener was a famous British general.

22

The Lion
by Jack Prelutsky

The lion has a golden mane
and under it a clever brain.
He lies around and idly roars
and lets the lioness do the chores.

A Bird
by Emily Dickinson

A bird came down the walk:
He did not know I saw;
He bit an angle-worm in halves
And ate the fellow, raw.

A Bug Sat in a Silver Flower
by Karla Kuskin

A bug sat in a silver flower
Thinking silver thoughts.
A bigger bug out for a walk
Climbed up that silver flower stalk
And snapped the small bug down his jaws
Without a pause
Without a care
For all the bug's small silver thoughts.
It isn't right
It isn't fair
That big bug ate that little bug
Because that little bug was there.
He also ate his underwear.

The Troll

by Jack Prelutsky

Be wary of the loathsome troll
that slyly lies in wait
to drag you to his dingy hole
and put you on his plate.

His blood is black and boiling hot,
he gurgles ghastly groans.
He'll cook you in his dinner pot,
your skin, your flesh, your bones.

He'll catch your arms and clutch your legs
and grind you to a pulp,
then swallow you like scrambled eggs—
gobble! gobble! gulp!

So watch your steps when next you go
upon a pleasant stroll,
or you might end in the pit below
as supper for the troll.

23

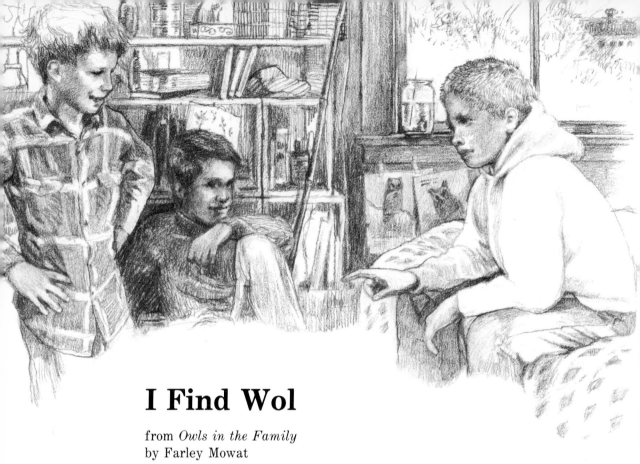

I Find Wol

from *Owls in the Family*
by Farley Mowat

Billy, Bruce, and Murray have lots of pets—dogs,
white rats, snakes, rabbits, and gophers. Then they
find the nest of a great horned owl. There are three
young owls in the nest. Of course, the boys think the
little owls would make great pets. But how are they to
get the owlets out of the nest?

☙ ☙ ☙

The next week seemed awfully long. The only time I
really hated school was during the springtime—
particularly in May when the birds were busy nesting
on the prairies. This May week, what with thinking
about the owls, and sitting by the open window
sniffing the smells of springtime, I wished school had
never been invented.

Every recess, and after school, Murray and Bruce
and I talked about the young owls and tried to think
of ways to get them out of their nest. Murray

suggested we should cut down the tree; but that was too dangerous because the young owls might be hurt. Bruce said he might get his father to come and shoot the old owl so it would be safe for us to climb the tree; but that wasn't fair.

The only thing I could think of was firecrackers. My idea was to get some small skyrockets and let them off under the nest to scare the mother owl away. The trouble was that we had no money and, anyway, the storekeepers wouldn't sell skyrockets to kids our age.

Then, on Friday night, we had a storm of the kind called a "chinook." Chinooks come down out of the Rocky Mountains in Alberta and sometimes they blow right across Saskatchewan—and they blow like fury. Lying in my bed on Friday night I could hear branches snapping off the poplar trees along the riverbank. The rain was pelting on the roof so hard that it scared Mutt (who always slept on my bed) and made him howl. I had to pull a quilt over his head to make him keep quiet. He hated storms. I worried about the young owls for a long time before I finally fell asleep.

Early on Saturday morning Murray called for me and we met Bruce at the Railroad Bridge. It was a fine morning and the sun kept popping in and out between the white clouds that were racing across the sky trying to catch up to the chinook. Everything was steaming from all the rain, and the prairie was soggy wet.

We hurried across the fields and didn't care if our feet did get soaked, because we were worried about the owls. When we were still quite a way from Owl Bluff, Bruce gave a shout:

"Lookee!" he yelled.

Sure enough, six or seven of the biggest cottonwoods were snapped right off at the tops. But the worst thing was the owl's-nest. The rain and wind had smashed it to pieces, and all that was left was a stick or two stuck in the crotch where the nest had been.

There was no sign of the old owls at all; but on the
ground near the foot of the tree were two young
owls—and they were cold and dead. They were so
young they had grown only about half their feathers,
and baby-down was still sticking to them all over. I
don't know whether they were killed by the fall, or not;
but they were as wet as sponges and I think they
probably died from being so wet and cold all night long.

We felt as miserable as could be, and all we could
think of to do was to have a funeral for the little owls.
Bruce had his jackknife with him and he started to dig
a grave while Murray and I went looking for the kind
of sticks to use for crosses. There was a big pile of
brush nearby, and I happened to give it a kick in
passing. Something went *snap-snap-snap* from under
it. I shoved my hand under the brush and touched a
bundle of wet feathers.

Bruce and Murray came over and we pulled the
brush away. There was the missing owlet, the third
one that had been in the nest, and he was still alive.

He was bigger than the other two, and that was

probably because he was the first one hatched. Horned
owls are funny that way. They begin to lay their eggs
in March when it's still winter on the prairie. The eggs
are laid a few days apart, but from the time the first
one is laid, the mother has to start "setting." If she
waited until she had a full clutch of eggs, the early
ones would be chilled and would never hatch. The first
egg that's laid hatches first, and that young owl gets a
four- or five-day head start on the next one who, in
turn, gets a head start on the next one.

   The one we found must have been the first to hatch
because he not only was bigger than the others but
must have been a lot stronger too. When the nest blew
apart, and he fell to the ground, he was able to wiggle
under the brush pile for shelter, and that probably
saved his life.

   He was about as big as a chicken, and you could see
his grown-up feathers pushing through the baby-down.
He even had the beginnings of the two "horn" feathers
growing on his head. A surprising thing about him was
that he was almost pure white, with only small black

markings on the ends of his feathers. When we found him he looked completely miserable, because all his down and feathers were stuck together in clumps, and he was shivering like a leaf.

I thought he would be too miserable to feel like fighting, but when I tried to pick him up he hunched forward, spread his wings, and hissed at me. It was a good try, but he was too weak to keep it up, and he fell right over on his face.

I was still a little bit afraid of him, because his claws were long and sharp, and his beak—which he kept snapping—seemed big enough to bite off my finger. But he did look so wet and sad that after a while I stopped being afraid. I got down on my knees in front of him and, very slowly, put my hand on his back. He hunched down as if he thought I was going to hurt him, but when I didn't hurt, he stopped hissing and lay still. He felt as cold as ice. I took off my shirt and put it over him, and then I picked him up as carefully as I could and carried him out of the bluff so he could sit in the sunshine and get dry and warm again.

It was surprising how fast he started to get better. In half an hour his feathers were dry and he was standing up and looking around him. Murray had brought along some roast-beef sandwiches for lunch. He took some meat out of the sandwiches and held it out to the owl. The owl looked at him a minute, with its head on one side, then it gave a funny little hop and came close enough to snatch the meat out of Murray's fingers. It gave a couple of gulps, blinked its eyes once, and the meat was gone.

He was certainly a hungry owl! He ate all the meat we had, and most of the bread as well. When I found some dead mice that his mother must have left on the edge of the nest, and which had also been blown to the ground, the owl ate them too. They must have been

hard to swallow, because he ate them whole. But he got them down somehow.

After that we were friends. When Bruce and I started to walk away from him, just to see what he would do, the owl followed right along behind us like a dog. He couldn't fly, of course; and he couldn't walk any too well either. He kind of jumped along, but he stayed right with us all the same. I think he knew he was an orphan, and that if he stayed with us we'd look after him.

When I sat down again, he came up beside me and, after taking a sideways look into my face, he hopped up on my leg. I was afraid his claws would go right through my skin, but they didn't hurt at all. He was being very careful.

"Guess he's your owl, all right," Bruce said, and I could see he was a little jealous.

"No, sir, Bruce," I replied. "He can live at my place, but he's going to be our owl—all three of us."

We left him sitting in the sun by the haversacks and then we buried the other two little owls and had a funeral over them. After that we were ready to go home.

We decided the best way to carry our new pet was to put him in my haversack. He didn't like it much, but after a struggle we managed to stuff him into it. We left his head sticking out so he could see where he was going.

Mutt and Bruce's dog, Rex, hadn't been with us that morning. I think the two of them had gone off cat-hunting before we got up. But as we were walking along the sidewalk in front of my house, we met old Mutt coming back from wherever he had been.

Mutt was cross-eyed and short-sighted, and so he never could see any too well. He came up to me to say hello, wagging his long tail and sniffing me—and then suddenly he smelled owl. I don't think he knew exactly what it was he smelled, because he had never been

close to an owl before. But he knew he smelled
something strange. I stood there trying not to laugh
while he sniffed all around me. He snuffed my
trousers and then he began to sniff the haversack.
When his nose was nearly in the owl's face, the bird
opened its beak and snapped it shut again right on the
end of poor old Mutt's black nose. Mutt gave a yelp
you could have heard a mile away, and went loping off
to hide his hurt feelings under the garage.

We put the owl in the summerhouse and when Dad
got home from work the owl was sitting on an orange
crate watching the gophers running around on the
floor below him. It kept him busy. His head kept
turning one way and then the other until it looked as
if he were going to unscrew it right off his shoulders.
He didn't know what to make of the gophers, because
he had never seen a live one before. But he was
certainly interested in them.

"Better count your gophers, Billy," said my father.
"I have an idea they may start disappearing. By the
way, what do you call your owl?"

I hadn't thought of any name for him up until that
moment, but now one just popped into my head. I
remembered Christopher Robin's owl in *Winnie-the-Pooh*.

"His name is Wol," I said.

And Wol he was, forever after.

If one owl is a good pet, are two owls better? You can
read about Billy's many funny adventures with his
owls in *Owls in the Family*. The author, Farley Mowat
(who is the Billy in this story) is one of Canada's
finest writers for young people. Another of his books
that you'll like is *The Dog Who Wouldn't Be*, which is
about the Mutt in this story. And to find out how owls
live in the wild, try *Bubo, The Great Horned Owl* by
John George and Jean Craighead George.

The Cow-Tail Switch

a West African folk tale

from *The Cow-Tail Switch and Other West African Stories*
by Harold Courlander and George Herzog

Near the edge of the Liberian rain forest, on a hill
overlooking the Cavally River, was the village of
Kundi. Its rice and cassava fields spread in all
directions. Cattle grazed in the grassland near the
river. Smoke from the fires in the round clay houses
seeped through the palm-leaf roofs, and from a
distance these faint columns of smoke seemed to hover
over the village. Men and boys fished in the river with
nets, and women pounded grain in wooden mortars
before the houses.

In this village, with his wife and many children,
lived a hunter by the name of Ogaloussa.

One morning Ogaloussa took his weapons down from
the wall of his house and went into the forest to hunt.
His wife and his children went to tend their fields, and
drove their cattle out to graze. The day passed, and
they ate their evening meal of manioc and fish.
Darkness came, but Ogaloussa didn't return.

Another day went by, and still Ogaloussa didn't
come back. They talked about it and wondered what
could have detained him. A week passed, then a month.
Sometimes Ogaloussa's sons mentioned that he hadn't
come home. The family cared for the crops, and the
sons hunted for game, but after a while they no longer
talked about Ogaloussa's disappearance.

Then, one day, another son was born to Ogaloussa's wife. His name was Puli. Puli grew older. He began to sit up and crawl. The time came when Puli began to talk, and the first thing he said was, "Where is my father?"

The other sons looked across the rice fields.

"Yes," one of them said. "Where is Father?"

"He should have returned long ago," another one said.

"Something must have happened. We ought to look for him," a third son said.

"He went into the forest, but where will we find him?" another one asked.

"I saw him go," one of them said. "He went that way, across the river. Let us follow the trail and search for him."

So the sons took their weapons and started out to

look for Ogaloussa. When they were deep among the great trees and vines of the forest they lost the trail. They searched in the forest until one of them found the trail again. They followed it until they lost the way once more, and then another son found the trail. It was dark in the forest, and many times they became lost. Each time another son found the way. At last they came to a clearing among the trees, and there on the ground scattered about lay Ogaloussa's bones and his rusted weapons. They knew then that Ogaloussa had been killed in the hunt.

One of the sons stepped forward and said, "I know how to put a dead person's bones together." He gathered all of Ogaloussa's bones and put them together, each in its right place.

Another son said, "I have knowledge too. I know how to cover the skeleton with sinews and flesh." He went to work, and he covered Ogaloussa's bones with sinews and flesh.

A third son said, "I have the power to put blood into a body." He went forward and put blood into Ogaloussa's veins, and then he stepped aside.

Another of the sons said, "I can put breath into a body." He did his work, and when he was through they saw Ogaloussa's chest rise and fall.

"I can give the power of movement to a body," another of them said. He put the power of movement into his father's body, and Ogaloussa sat up and opened his eyes.

"I can give him the power of speech," another son said. He gave the body the power of speech, and then he stepped back.

Ogaloussa looked around him. He stood up.

"Where are my weapons?" he asked.

They picked up his rusted weapons from the grass where they lay and gave them to him. They then returned the way they had come, through the forest and the rice fields, until they had arrived once more in the village.

Ogaloussa went into his house. His wife prepared a bath for him and he bathed. She prepared food for him and he ate. Four days he remained in the house, and on the fifth day he came out and shaved his head, because this was what people did when they came back from the land of the dead.

Afterwards he killed a cow for a great feast. He took the cow's tail and braided it. He decorated it with beads and cowry shells and bits of shiny metal. It was a beautiful thing. Ogaloussa carried it with him to important affairs. When there was a dance or an important ceremony he always had it with him. The people of the village thought it was the most beautiful cow-tail switch they had ever seen.

Soon there was a celebration in the village because Ogaloussa had returned from the dead. The people dressed in their best clothes, the musicians brought out their instruments, and a big dance began. The drummers beat their drums and the women sang. The people drank much palm wine. Everyone was happy.

Ogaloussa carried his cow-tail switch, and everyone admired it. Some of the men grew bold and came forward to Ogaloussa and asked for the cow-tail switch, but Ogaloussa kept it in his hand. Now and then there was a clamor and much confusion as many people asked for it at once. The women and children begged for it too, but Ogaloussa refused them all.

Finally he stood up to talk. The dancing stopped and people came close to hear what Ogaloussa had to say.

"A long time ago I went into the forest," Ogaloussa said. "While I was hunting I was killed by a leopard. Then my sons came for me. They brought me back from the land of the dead to my village. I will give this cow-tail switch to one of my sons. All of them have done something to bring me back from the dead, but I have only one cow-tail to give. I shall give it to the one who did the most to bring me home."

So an argument started.

"He will give it to me!" one of the sons said. "It was I who did the most, for I found the trail in the forest when it was lost!"

"No, he will give it to me!" another son said. "It was I who put his bones together!"

"It was I who covered his bones with sinews and flesh!" another said. "He will give it to me!"

"It was I who gave him the power of movement!" another son said. "I deserve it most!"

Another son said it was he who should have the switch, because he had put blood in Ogaloussa's veins. Another claimed it because he had put breath in the body. Each of the sons argued his right to possess the wonderful cow-tail switch.

Before long not only the sons but the other people of the village were talking. Some of them argued that the son who had put blood in Ogaloussa's veins should get the switch, others that the one who had given

Ogaloussa's breath should get it. Some of them believed that all of the sons had done equal things, and that they should share it. They argued back and forth this way until Ogaloussa asked them to be quiet.

"To this son I will give the cow-tail switch, for I owe most to him," Ogaloussa said.

He came forward and bent low and handed it to Puli, the little boy who had been born while Ogaloussa was in the forest.

The people of the village remembered then that the child's first words had been, "Where is my father?" They knew that Ogaloussa was right.

For it was a saying among them that a man is not really dead until he is forgotten.

In *The Cow-Tail Switch and Other West African Stories*, you will find seventeen more wonderful tales. Other books of African folk tales, all written or coauthored by Harold Courlander, include *Olode the Hunter and Other Tales from Nigeria*, *The Hat-Shaking Dance and Other Ashanti Tales from Ghana*, and *The King's Drum and Other African Stories*.

Limericks

A limerick is a clever and witty form of verse. It consists of five short lines. The first two lines always rhyme with the fifth line. No one knows who invented the form, but it takes its name from the city of Limerick in Ireland. The English writer and artist Edward Lear made limericks popular. His first book of poems, *A Book of Nonsense* (1846), contained more than two hundred humorous limericks.

There was an Old Man with a beard,
Who said, "It is just as I feared!
  Two Owls and a Hen,
  Four Larks and a Wren
Have all built their nests in my beard."

by Edward Lear

There was an Old Person of Ware,
Who rode on the back of a bear.
    When they asked, "Does it trot?"
    He said, "Certainly *not!*
It's a Moppsikon Floppsikon bear!"

                    by Edward Lear

There was a Young Maid who asked, "Why
Can't I look in my ear with my eye?
    If I give my mind to it,
    I'm sure I can do it,
You never can tell till you try."

                    by Edward Lear

An epicure dining at Crewe
Once found a large mouse in his stew.
    Said the waiter, "Don't shout
    And wave it about,
Or the rest will be wanting one, too!"

                    author unknown

There was a Young Woman named Bright,
Whose speed was much faster than light.
    She set out one day
    In a relative way,
And returned on the previous night.

                    author unknown

There was a Faith Healer of Deal,
Who said, "Although pain isn't real,
    If I sit on a pin,
    And it punctures my skin,
I dislike what I fancy I feel."

                    author unknown

There was an Old Man who said, "Do
Tell me *how* I should add two and two?
  I think more and more
  That it makes about four—
But I fear that is almost too few."

author unknown

An indolent vicar of Bray
Let his lovely red roses decay;
  His wife, more alert,
  Bought a powerful squirt,
And said to her spouse, "Let us spray."

author unknown

A fly and a flea in a flue
Were imprisoned, so what could they do?
  Said the fly, "Let us flee!"
  "Let us fly!" said the flea.
So they flew through a flaw in the flue.

author unknown

There was an Old Man from Peru
Who dreamed he was eating his shoe.
  He woke in a fright
  In the middle of the night
And found it was perfectly true.

author unknown

A cheerful Old Bear at the Zoo
Could always find something to do.
  When it bored him to go
  On a walk to and fro,
He reversed it, and walked fro and to.

author unknown

There was a Young Lady of Lynn,
Who was so uncommonly thin
  That when she essayed
  To drink lemonade,
She slipped through the straw and fell in.

author unknown

The bottle of perfume that Willie sent
Was highly displeasing to Millicent.
  Her thanks were so cold
  That they quarreled, I'm told,
Through that silly scent Willie sent Millicent.

author unknown

There was a Young Lady of Crete,
Who was so exceedingly neat,
  When she got out of bed
  She stood on her head,
To make sure of not soiling her feet.

author unknown

There once was a Young Man named Hall
Who fell in the spring in the fall.
  'Twould have been a sad thing
  Had he died in the spring,
But he didn't—he died in the fall.

author unknown

There was a Young Lady of Niger
Who smiled as she rode on a tiger.
  They came back from the ride
  With the lady inside
And the smile on the face of the tiger.

author unknown

Harriet's Secret

from *Harriet the Spy*
by Louise Fitzhugh

Eleven-year-old Harriet wants to be a writer. To
prepare for her future career, she keeps a notebook in
which she jots down what she sees and thinks. The
problem is that she gets her material by spying on
people, especially her friends at the private school she
attends in New York. And this leads to trouble.

That day, after school, everyone felt in a good mood
because the weather was suddenly gay and soft like
spring. They hung around outside, the whole class
together, which was something they never did. Sport
said suddenly, "Hey, why don't we go to the park and
play tag?"

Harriet was late for her spying, but she thought she
would just play one game and then leave. They all
seemed to think this was a smashing idea, so everyone
filed across the street.

The kind of tag they played wasn't very complicated;
in fact Harriet thought it was rather silly. The object
seemed to be to run around in circles and get very
tired, then whoever was "it" tried to knock everyone

else's books out of their arms. They played and played. Beth Ellen was eliminated at once, having no strength. Sport was the best. He managed to knock down everyone's books except Rachel Hennessey's and Harriet's.

He ran round and round then, very fast. Suddenly he knocked a few of Harriet's things off her arms, then Rachel tried to tease him away, and Harriet started to run like crazy. Soon she was running and running as fast as she could in the direction of the mayor's house. Rachel was right after her and Sport was close behind.

They ran and ran along the river. Then they were on the grass and Sport fell down. It wasn't any fun with him not chasing, so Rachel and Harriet waited until he got up. Then he was very quick and got them.

All of Rachel's books were on the ground, and some of Harriet's. They began to pick them up to go back and join the others.

Suddenly Harriet screeched in horror, "Where is my notebook?" They all began looking around, but they couldn't find it anywhere. Harriet suddenly remembered that some things had been knocked down before they ran away from the others. She began to run back toward them. She ran and ran, yelling like a banshee the whole way.

When she got back to where they had started she saw the whole class—Beth Ellen, Pinky Whitehead, Carrie Andrews, Marion Hawthorne, Laura Peters, and The Boy with the Purple Socks—all sitting around a bench while Janie Gibbs read to them from the notebook.

Harriet descended upon them with a scream that was supposed to frighten Janie so much she would drop the book. But Janie didn't frighten easily. She just stopped reading and looked up calmly. The others looked up too. She looked at all their eyes and suddenly Harriet M. Welsch was afraid.

They just looked and looked, and their eyes were the meanest eyes she had ever seen. They formed a little knot and wouldn't let her near them. Rachel and Sport came up then. Marion Hawthorne said fiercely, "Rachel, come over here." Rachel walked over to her, and after Marion had whispered in her ear, got the same mean look.

Janie said, "Sport, come over here."

"Whadaya mean?" said Sport.

"I have something to tell you," Janie said in a very pointed way.

Sport walked over and Harriet's heart went into her sneakers. "FINKS!" Harriet felt rather hysterical. She didn't know what that word meant, but since her father said it all the time, she knew it was bad.

Janie passed the notebook to Sport and Rachel,

never taking her eyes off Harriet as she did so. "Sport,
you're on page thirty-four; Rachel, you're on fifteen,"
she said quietly.

Sport read his and burst into tears. "Read it aloud,
Sport," said Janie harshly.

"I can't." Sport hid his face.

The book was passed back to Janie. Janie read the
passage in a solemn voice.

*Sometimes I can't stand Sport. With his worrying all
the time and fussing over his father, sometimes he's
like a little old woman.*

Sport turned his back on Harriet, but even from his
back Harriet could see that he was crying.

"That's not *fair*," she screamed. "There're some nice
things about Sport in there."

Everyone got very still. Janie spoke very quietly. "Harriet, go over there on that bench until we decide what we're going to do to you."

Harriet went over and sat down. She couldn't hear them. They began to discuss something rapidly with many gestures. Sport kept his back turned and Janie never took her eyes off Harriet, no matter who was talking.

Harriet thought suddenly, I don't have to sit here. And she got up and marched off in as dignified a way as possible under the circumstances. They were so busy they didn't even seem to notice her.

At home, eating her cake and milk, Harriet reviewed her position. It was terrible. She decided that she had never been in a worse position. She then decided she wasn't going to think about it anymore. She went to bed in the middle of the afternoon and didn't get up until the next morning.

Her mother thought she was sick and said to her father, "Maybe we ought to call the doctor."

"Finks, all of them," said her father. Then they went away and Harriet went to sleep.

In the park all the children sat around and read things aloud. These are some of the things they read:

Notes on what Carrie Andrews thinks of Marion Hawthorne
> *Thinks: Is mean*
> > *Is rotten in math*
> > *Has funny knees*
> > *Is a pig*

Then:

If Marion Hawthorne doesn't watch out she's going to grow up into a lady Hitler.

Janie Gibbs smothered a laugh at that one but not at the next one:

Who does Janie Gibbs think she's kidding? Does she really think she could ever be a scientist?

Janie looked as though she had been struck. Sport looked at her sympathetically. They looked at each other, in fact, in a long, meaningful way.

Janie read on:

What to do about Pinky Whitehead

> *1. Turn the hose on him.*
> *2. Pinch his ears until he screams.*
> *3. Tear his pants off and laugh at him.*

Pinky felt like running. He looked around nervously, but Harriet was nowhere to be seen.

There was something about everyone.

Maybe Beth Ellen doesn't have any parents. I asked her her mother's name and she couldn't remember. She said she had only seen her once and she didn't remember it very well. She wears strange things like orange sweaters and a big black car comes for her once a week and she goes someplace else.

Beth Ellen rolled her big eyes and said nothing. She never said anything, so this wasn't unusual.

The reason Sport dresses so funny is that his father won't buy him anything to wear because his mother has all the money.

Sport turned his back again.

Today a new boy arrived. He is so dull no one can remember his name so I have named him The Boy with the Purple Socks. Imagine. Where would he ever find purple socks?

The Boy with the Purple Socks looked down at his purple socks and smiled.

Everyone looked at the sock boy. Carrie spoke up. She had a rather grating voice. "What *IS* your name?" even though by now they all knew perfectly well.

"Peter," he said shyly.

"Why *do* you wear purple socks?" asked Janie.

Peter smiled shyly, looked at his socks, then said, "Once, at the circus, my mother lost me. She said, after that, if I had on purple socks, she could always find me."

"Hmmmmm," said Janie.

Gathering courage from this, Peter spoke again. "She *wanted* to make it a whole purple suit, but I rebelled."

"I don't blame you," said Janie.

Peter bobbed his head and grinned. They all grinned back at him because he had a tooth missing and looked rather funny, but also he wasn't a bad sort, so they all began to like him a little bit.

They read on:

Miss Elson has a wart behind her elbow:

This was fairly boring so they skipped ahead.

I once saw Miss Elson when she didn't see me and she was picking her nose.

That was better, but still they wanted to read about themselves.

Carrie Andrews' mother has the biggest front I ever saw.

There was a great deal of tension in the group after this last item. Then Sport gave a big horselaugh, and Pinky Whitehead's ears turned bright red. Janie smiled a fierce and frightening smile at Carrie Andrews, who looked as though she wanted to dive under the bench.

When I grow up I'm going to find out everything about everybody and put it all in a book. The book is going to be called Secrets *by Harriet M. Welsch. I will also have photographs in it and maybe some medical charts if I can get them.*

Rachel stood up, "I have to go home. Is there anything about me?"

They flipped through until they found her name.

I don't know exactly if I like Rachel or whether it is just that I like going to her house because her mother makes homemade cake. If I had a club I'm not sure I would have Rachel in it.

"Thank you," Rachel said politely and left for home. Laura Peters left too after the last item:

If Laura Peters doesn't stop smiling at me in that wishy-washy way I'm going to give her a good kick.

The next morning when Harriet arrived at school no one spoke to her. They didn't even look at her. It was exactly as though no one at all had walked into the room. Harriet sat down and felt like a lump. She looked at everyone's desk, but there was no sign of the notebook. She looked at every face and on every face was a plan, and on each face was the same plan. They had organization. I'm going to get it, she thought grimly.

That was not the worst of it. The worst was that even though she knew she shouldn't, she had stopped by the stationery store on the way to school and had bought another notebook. She had tried not to write in it, but she was such a creature of habit that even now she found herself taking it out of the pocket of her jumper, and furthermore, the next minute she was scratching in a whole series of things.

They are out to get me. The whole room is filled with mean eyes. I won't get through the day. I might throw up my tomato sandwich. Even Sport and Janie. What did I say about Janie? I don't remember. Never mind. They may think I am a weakling but a spy is trained for this kind of fight. I am ready for them.

She went on scratching until Miss Elson cleared her throat, signifying she had entered the room. Then everyone stood up as they always did, bowed, said, "Good morning, Miss Elson," and sat back down. It was the custom at this moment for everyone to punch each other. Harriet looked around for someone to do some poking with, but they all sat stony-faced as though they had never poked anyone in their whole lives.

It made Harriet feel better to try and quote like Ole Golly,[1] so she wrote:

The sins of the fathers

That was all she knew from the Bible besides the shortest verse: "Jesus wept."

Class began and all was forgotten in the joy of writing Harriet M. Welsch at the top of the page.

Halfway through the class Harriet saw a tiny piece of paper float to the floor on her right. Ah-ha, she thought, the chickens; they are making up already. She reached down to get the note. A hand flew past her nose and she realized that the note had been retrieved in a neat backhand by Janie who sat to the right of her.

Well, she thought, so it wasn't for me, that's all. She looked at Carrie, who had sent the note, and Carrie looked carefully away without even giggling.

Harriet wrote in her notebook:

Carrie Andrews has an ugly pimple right next to her nose.

Feeling better, she attacked her homework with renewed zeal. She was getting hungry. Soon she would

---

1. Ole Golly is Harriet's nursemaid.

have her tomato sandwich. She looked up at Miss Elson who was looking at Marion Hawthorne who was scratching her knee. As Harriet looked back at her work she suddenly saw a glint of white sticking out of Janie's jumper pocket. It was the note! Perhaps she could just reach over ever so quietly and pull back very quickly. She *had* to see.

She watched her own arm moving very quietly over, inch by inch. Was Carrie Andrews watching? No. Another inch. Another. *There!!* She had it. Janie obviously hadn't felt a thing. Now to read! She looked at Miss Elson but she seemed to be in a dream. She unfolded the tiny piece of paper and read:

Harriet M. Welsch smells. Don't you think so?

Oh, no! Did she really smell? What of? Bad, obviously. Must be very bad. She held up her hand and got excused from class. She went into the bathroom and smelled herself all over, but she couldn't smell anything bad. Then she washed her hands and face. She was going to leave, then she went back and washed her feet just in case. Nothing smelled. What were they talking about? Anyway, now, just to be sure, they would smell of soap.

When she got back to her desk, she noticed a little piece of paper next to where her foot would ordinarily be when she sat down. Ah, this will explain it, she thought. She made a swift move, as though falling, and retrieved the note without Miss Elson seeing. She unrolled it eagerly and read:

There is nothing that makes me sicker than watching Harriet M. Welsch eat a tomato sandwich.
                                        Pinky Whitehead

The note must have misfired. Pinky sat to the right and it was addressed to Sport, who sat on her left.

What was sickening about a tomato sandwich? Harriet felt the taste in her mouth. Were they crazy?

It was the best taste in the world. Her mouth watered at the memory of the mayonnaise. It was an experience, as Mrs. Welsch was always saying. How could it make anyone sick? Pinky Whitehead was what could make you sick. Those stick legs and the way his neck seemed to swivel up and down away from his body. She wrote in her notebook:

There is no rest for the weary.

As she looked up she saw Marion Hawthorne turn swiftly in her direction. Then suddenly she was looking full at Marion Hawthorne's tongue out at her, and a terribly ugly face around the tongue, with eyes all screwed up and pulled down by two fingers so that the whole thing looked as though Marion Hawthorne were going to be carted away to the hospital. Harriet glanced quickly at Miss Elson. Miss Elson was dreaming out the window. Harriet wrote quickly:

How unlike Marion Hawthorne. I don't think she ever did anything bad.

Then she heard the giggles. She looked up. Everyone had caught the look. Everyone was giggling and laughing with Marion, even Sport and Janie. Miss Elson turned around and every face went blank, everybody bent again over the desks. Harriet wrote quietly.

Perhaps I can talk to my mother about changing schools. I have the feeling this morning that everyone in this school is insane. I might possibly bring a ham sandwich tomorrow but I have to think about it.

The lunch bell rang. Everyone jumped as though they had one body and pushed out the door. Harriet jumped too, but for some reason or other three people bumped into her as she did. It was so fast she didn't even see who it was, but the way they did it she was pushed so far back that she was the last one out the door. They all ran ahead, had gotten their lunchboxes, and were outside by the time she got to the cloakroom. It's true that she was detained because she had to make a note of the fact that Miss Elson went to the science room to talk to Miss Maynard, which had never happened before in the history of the school.

When she picked up her lunch the bag felt very light. She reached inside and there was only crumpled paper. They had taken her tomato sandwich. They had *taken* her tomato sandwich. Someone had *taken* it. She couldn't get over it. This was completely against the rules of the school. No one was supposed to steal your tomato sandwich. She had been coming to this school since she was four—let's see, that made seven years—and in all those seven years no one had ever taken her tomato sandwich. Not even during those six months when she had brought pickle sandwiches with mustard. No one had even asked for so much as a bite. Sometimes Beth Ellen passed around olives because no one else had olives and they were very chic, but that was the extent of the sharing. And now here it was noon and she had nothing to eat.

She was aghast. What could she do? It would be ridiculous to go around asking "Has anyone seen a tomato sandwich?" They were sure to laugh. She would go to Miss Elson. No, then she would be a ratter, a squealer, a stoolie. Well, she couldn't starve. She went to the telephone and asked to use it because she had forgotten her lunch. She called and the cook told her to come home, that she would make another tomato sandwich in the meantime.

Harriet left, went home, ate her tomato sandwich, and took to her bed for another day. She had to think. Her mother was playing bridge downtown. She pretended to be sick enough so the cook didn't yell at her and yet not sick enough for the cook to call her mother. She had to think.

As she lay there in the half gloom she looked out

over the trees in the park. For a while she watched a bird, then an old man who walked like a drunk. Inside she felt herself thinking "Everybody hates me, everybody hates me."

At first she didn't listen to it and then she heard what she was feeling. She said it several times to hear it better. Then she reached nervously for her notebook and wrote in big, block letters, the way she used to write when she was little.

EVERYBODY HATES ME.

She leaned back and thought about it. It was time for her cake and milk, so she got up and went downstairs in her pajamas to have it. The cook started a fight with her, saying that if she were sick she couldn't have any cake and milk.

Harriet felt big hot tears come to her eyes and she started to scream.

The cook said calmly, "Either you go to school and you come home and have your cake and milk, or you are sick and you don't get cake and milk because that's no good for you when you're sick; but you don't lie around up there all day and then get cake and milk."

"That's the most unreasonable thing I ever heard of," Harriet screamed. She began to scream as loud as she could. Suddenly she heard herself saying over and over again, "I hate you, I hate you, I hate you." Even as she did it she knew she didn't really hate the cook; in fact, she rather liked her, but it seemed to her that at that moment she hated her.

The cook turned her back and Harriet heard her mutter, "Oh, you, you hate everybody."

This was too much. Harriet ran to her room. She did not hate everybody. She did not. Everybody hated her, that's all. She crashed into her room with a bang, ran to her bed, and smashed her face down into the pillow.

After she was tired of crying, she lay there and looked at the trees. She saw a bird and began to hate the bird. She saw the old drunk man and felt such hatred for him she almost fell off the bed. Then she thought of them all and she hated them each and every one in turn: Carrie Andrews, Marion Hawthorne, Rachel Hennessey, Beth Ellen Hansen, Laura Peters, Pinky Whitehead, the new one with the purple socks, and even Sport and Janie, especially Sport and Janie.

She just hated them. I *hate* them, she thought. She picked up her notebook:

When I am big I will be a spy. I will go to one country and I will find out its secrets and then I will go to another country and tell them and then find out their secrets and I will go back to the first one and rat on the second and I will go to the second and rat on the first. I will be the best spy there ever was and I will know everything. Everything.

As she began to fall asleep she thought, And then they'll all be petrified of me.

Harriet was sick for three days. That is, she lay in bed for three days. Then her mother took her to see the kindly old family doctor. He used to be a kindly old family doctor who made house calls, but now he wouldn't anymore. One day he had stamped his foot at Harriet's mother and said, "I like my office and I'm going to stay in it. I pay so much rent on this office that if I leave it for five minutes my child misses a year of school. I'm never coming out again." And from that moment on he didn't. Harriet rather respected him for it, but his stethoscope was cold.

When he had looked Harriet all over, he said to her mother, "There isn't a blessed thing wrong with her."

Harriet's mother gave her a dirty look, then sent her out into the outer office. As Harriet closed the door behind her she heard the doctor saying, "I think I know what's the matter with her. Carrie told us some long story about a notebook."

Harriet stopped dead in her tracks. "That's right,"

she said out loud to herself. "His name is Dr. Andrews, so he's Carrie Andrews' father."

She got out her notebook and wrote it down. Then she wrote:

I wonder why he doesn't cure that pimple on Carrie's nose?

"Come on, young lady, we're going home." Harriet's mother took her by the hand. She looked as though she might take Harriet home and kill her. As it turned out, she didn't. When they got home, she said briskly, "All right, Harriet the Spy, come into the library and talk to me."

Harriet followed her, dragging her feet. She wished she were Beth Ellen who had never met her mother.

"Now, Harriet, I hear you're keeping dossiers on everyone in school."

"What's that?" Harriet had been prepared to deny everything but this was a new one.

"You keep a notebook?"

"A notebook?"

"Well, don't you?"

"Why?"

"Answer me, Harriet." It was serious.

"Yes."

"What did you put in it?"

"Everything."

"Well, what kind of thing?"

"Just . . . things."

"Harriet Welsch, answer me. What do you write about your classmates?"

"Oh, just . . . well, things I think. . . . Some nice things . . . and—and mean things."

"And your friends saw it?"

"Yes, but they shouldn't have looked. It's private. It even says PRIVATE all over the front of it."

"Nevertheless, they did. Right?"

"Yes."

"And then what happened?"

"Nothing."

"Nothing?" Harriet's mother looked very skeptical.

"Well . . . my tomato sandwich disappeared."

"Don't you think that maybe all those mean things made them angry?"

Harriet considered this as though it had never entered her mind. "Well, maybe, but they shouldn't have looked. It's private property."

"That, Harriet, is beside the point. They *did*. Now why do you think they got angry?"

"I don't know."

"Well . . ." Mrs. Welsch seemed to be debating whether to say what she finally did. "How did you feel when you got some of those notes?"

There was a silence. Harriet looked at her feet.

"Harriet?" Her mother was waiting for an answer.

"I think I feel sick again. I think I'll go to bed."

"Now, darling, you're not sick. Just think about it a moment. How did you feel?"

Harriet burst into tears. She ran to her mother and cried very hard. "I felt awful. I felt awful," was all she could say. Her mother hugged her and kissed her a lot. The more she hugged her the better Harriet felt. She was still being hugged when her father came home. He hugged her too, even though he didn't know what it was all about. After that they all had dinner and Harriet went up to bed.

How do you think Harriet will work out her problems? You can find out by reading the book, *Harriet the Spy*, by Louise Fitzhugh. And you can follow her further adventures in *The Long Secret*. Another book you will enjoy is *The Secret Language* by Ursula Nordstrom. It is about two girls at a boarding school and the "secret language" they share.

The Old Man with the Bump

from *The Dancing Kettle and Other Japanese Folk Tales* retold by Yoshiko Uchida

Long, long ago, there lived an old man who had a large bump on his right cheek. It grew larger and larger each day, and he could do nothing to make it go away.

"Oh, dear, how will I ever rid myself of this bump on my cheek," sighed the old man; and though he went from doctor to doctor throughout the countryside, not one of them could help him.

"You have been a good and honest man," said his wife. "Surely some day there will be someone who can help you."

And so, the old man kept hoping each day that this "someone" would come along soon.

Now one day the old man went out into the hills to collect some sticks for his fire. When the sun began to dip behind the hills, he strapped a large bundle of wood on his back and slowly began the long walk back to his little house at the foot of the hill. Suddenly the sky began to darken, and soon huge drops of rain splashed down on the wooded hillside. The old man hurriedly looked about for some shelter, and before long spied a gnarled old pine tree with a large hollow in its trunk.

"Ah, that will be a good shelter for me during the storm," he said to himself, and he quickly crawled into the hollow of the tree. He did this just in time too, for

soon the rain poured down from the skies as though
someone had overturned an immense barrel of water
up in the heavens. The old man crouched low as the
thunder crashed above his head and the lightning
made weird streaks of light in the dark forest.

"My, what a storm this is!" he said to himself, and
closed his eyes tight. But it was just a thundershower,
and it stopped as suddenly as it had begun. Soon, all
the old man could hear was the drip, drop . . . of the
rain slipping down from the shiny pine needles.

"Ah, now that the rain has stopped I must hurry
home, or my wife will worry about me," said the old
man.

He was about to crawl out of the hollow of the tree,
when he heard a rustling like the sound of many,
many people walking through the forest.

"Well, there must have been other men caught in the
forest by the storm," he thought, and he waited to
walk home with them. But suddenly the old man
turned pale as he saw who was making the sounds he

had heard. He turned with a leap, and jumped right back into the hollow of the tree. For the footsteps weren't made by men at all. They were made by many, many ghosts and spirits walking straight toward the old man.

The old man was so frightened he wanted to cry out for help, but he knew no one could help him.

"Oh, dear, ohhhh, dear," moaned the old man, as he buried his head in his hands. "What will they do to me?"

But soon he raised his head ever so slightly, for he thought he heard music in the air. Yes, there were singing voices and laughing voices floating toward him. The old man lifted his head a little more and ever so carefully took a peek to see what they were doing. His mouth fell wide open in surprise at the sight before his eyes. The spirits were gaily dancing about on the soft carpet of pine needles. They laughed and sang as they whirled and twirled about. They were feasting, and drinking, and making merry.

"A feast of spirits! My, I have never seen such a strange sight," said the old man to himself. Soon he forgot to be afraid and he poked his head further and further from the hollow of the tree. The old man's feet began to tap in time to the music, and he clapped his hands along with the spirits. His head swayed from side to side and he smiled happily as he watched the strange sight before him.

Now he could hear the leader saying, "Such foolish dances! I want to see some really fine dancing. Is there no one here who can do any better?"

Before he knew what he was doing, the old man had jumped right out of the hole, and danced out among the ghosts.

"Here, I will show you something different! I will show you some fine dancing," he called. The spirits stepped back in surprise and the old man began to dance before them. With so many spirits watching

him, the old man did his very best, and danced as he
had never danced before.

"Good, very good indeed," said the leader of the
spirits, nodding his head in time to the music.

"Yes, yes," agreed the others. "We have never seen
such fine dancing!"

When the old man stopped, the spirits crowded about
him, offering him food and drink from their feast.

"Thank you, thank you," said the old man happily.
He breathed a sigh of relief as he saw that he had
pleased the spirits, for he had feared that they might
harm a mortal such as he.

The leader of the spirits then stepped before the old
man and said in a deep, low voice, "We would like to
see more of such fine dancing. Will you return again
tomorrow, old man?"

"Yes, yes, of course I will come," answered the old
man, but the other spirits shook their ghostly heads
and lifted warning fingers.

"Perhaps this mortal will not keep his word," they
protested. "Let us take a forfeit from him—something

which he treasures most—then he will be sure to return for it tomorrow."

"Ah, a fine plan indeed," answered the leader. "What shall we take from him?"

All the spirits stepped around the old man, and examined him from head to toe to see what would make a good forfeit.

"Shall it be his cap?" asked one.

"Or his jacket?" asked another.

Then finally one spoke up in a loud and happy voice, "The bump on his cheek! The bump on his cheek! Take that from him and he will be sure to come for it tomorrow, for I have heard that such bumps bring good luck to human beings, and that they treasure them greatly."

"Then that shall be the forfeit we will take," said the leader, and with one flick of his ghostly finger he snatched away the bump on the old man's cheek. Before he could say, "Oh," the spirits had all disappeared into the dusky woods.

The old man was so surprised he scarcely knew what to do. He looked at the spot where the spirits had just been standing and then rubbed the smooth, flat cheek where once the bump had been.

"My goodness! My, my," murmured the old man. Then with a big smile on his face he turned and hurried home.

Now, the old woman had been very worried, for she was afraid that the old man had met with an accident during the storm. She stood in the doorway of their cottage waiting for him to return, and when at last she saw him trudging down the road, she hastened to greet him.

"My, but I was worried about you," she said. "Did you get drenched in that thundershower?" Then suddenly the old woman stopped talking and looked carefully at the old man.

"Why, wh-hy, where is the bump on your right cheek? Surely you had it this morning when you went out into the woods!"

The old man laughed happily and told the old woman all about his meeting with the spirits. "So you see, I have lost my bump at last!" he added.

"My, isn't that nice!" exclaimed the old woman, admiring the old man's right cheek. "We must celebrate this happy occasion," she said, and together they feasted with *akano gohan* and *tai*.

Early the next morning they heard a knock on their door, and there stood the greedy man who lived next door to them. He had come to borrow some food, as he so often did.

Now this man also had a bump on his cheek, but his was on the left side of his face. When he saw the old man without his bump, he threw up his hands in surprise and exclaimed. "Why, what has happened? Where is the bump on your face?" He peered closely at the old man's face and said, "How I would like to get

rid of mine too! Perhaps I can if I do exactly as you did." Then, because he wanted the same good fortune, he asked anxiously, "Tell me, exactly what did you do?"

So the old man carefully explained how he hid in the hollow of an old tree until the spirits came to dance in the dusk. Then he told about the dance he did for them and how they took his bump for a forfeit.

"Ah, thank you, my friend," said the neighbor. "Tonight I shall do exactly the same thing." And after borrowing a large sack of the old man's rice, he hurried home.

That evening, the greedy neighbor trudged out into the woods and found the same tree. He slipped into the hollow trunk and waited quietly, peeking out every once in a while to watch for the spirits. Just as the sky began to darken and the setting sun painted all the clouds in gold, the spirits again twirled and whirled out into the small clearing in front of the old tree.

The leader looked about and said, "I wonder if the old man who danced for us yesterday will soon be here?"

"Yes, yes. Here I am!" cried the greedy neighbor, as he leaped from the hollow tree trunk. He opened out a fan and then he began his dance. But alas and alack, this old man had never learned how to dance. He hopped from one foot to the other, and shook his head from side to side, but the spirits were not smiling as they had been the day before. Instead they scowled and frowned, and called out, "This is terrible. We have no use for you, old man. Here, take back your precious bump," and with a big THUMP the leader flung the

bump on the greedy man's right cheek. Then the spirits disappeared into the woods just as quickly as they had come.

"Ohhhhh!" cried the greedy man as he sadly walked home. "Never again will I try to be someone else."

Now he not only had a big bump on his left cheek, he had one on his right cheek too. And so the greedy man who had tried to copy his neighbor went home looking just like a chipmunk with both cheeks full of nuts!

In the book from which this story came, *The Dancing Kettle and Other Japanese Folk Tales*, there are many other fine stories. Yoshiko Uchida has also written *The Magic Listening Cap: More Folk Tales from Japan* and *The Sea of Gold and Other Tales from Japan* (a story from this book is in Volume 9 of *Childcraft*). Or, try *The Golden Crane* by Tohr Yamaguichi.

The New Kid

by Mike Makley

Our baseball team never did very much,
we had me and PeeWee and Earl and Dutch.
And the Oak Street Tigers always got beat
until the new kid moved in on our street.

The kid moved in with a mitt and a bat
and an official New York Yankee hat.
The new kid plays shortstop or second base
and can outrun us all in any race.

The kid never muffs a grounder or fly
no matter how hard it's hit or how high.
And the new kid always acts quite polite,
never yelling or spitting or starting a fight.

We were playing the league champs just last week;
they were trying to break our winning streak.
In the last inning the score was one-one,
when the new kid swung and hit a home run.

A few of the kids and their parents say
they don't believe that the new kid should play.
But she's good as me, Dutch, PeeWee, or Earl,
so we don't care that the new kid's a girl.

Associations

by Eve Merriam

Home to me is not a house
Filled with family faces;
Home is where I slide in free
By rounding all the bases.

A tie to me is not
Clothing like a hat;
It means the game is even up
And I wish I were at bat.

Good Sportsmanship
by Richard Armour

Good sportsmanship we hail, we sing,
   It's always pleasant when you spot it.
There's only one unhappy thing:
    You have to lose to prove you've got it.

The Base Stealer
by Robert Francis

Poised between going on and back, pulled
Both ways taut like a tightrope-walker,
Fingertips pointing the opposites,
Now bouncing tiptoe like a dropped ball
Or a kid skipping rope, come on, come on,
Running a scattering of steps sidewise,
How he teeters, skitters, tingles, teases,
Taunts them, hovers like an ecstatic bird,
He's only flirting, crowd him, crowd him,
Delicate, delicate, delicate, delicate—now!

Foul Shot

by Edwin A. Hoey

With two 60's stuck on the scoreboard
And two seconds hanging on the clock,
The solemn boy in the center of eyes,
Squeezed by silence,
Seeks out the line with his feet,
Soothes his hands along his uniform,
Gently drums the ball against the floor,
Then measures the waiting net,
Raises the ball on his right hand,
Balances it with his left,
Calms it with fingertips,
Breathes,
Crouches,
Waits,
And then through a stretching of stillness,
Nudges it upward.
The ball slides up and out.
Lands,
Leans,
Wobbles,
Wavers,
Hesitates,
Exasperates,
Plays it coy
Until every face begs with unsounding
　　screams—
And then
　　And then,
　　　And then,
Right before ROAR-UP,
Dives down and through.

The Sidewalk Racer
OR
On the Skateboard
by Lillian Morrison

Skimming
an asphalt sea
I swerve, I curve, I
sway; I speed to whirring
sound an inch above the
ground; I'm the sailor
and the sail, I'm the
driver and the wheel
I'm the one and only
single engine
human auto
mobile.

The Knockout
by Lillian Morrison

The shortest fight
I ever saw
Was a left to the body
And a right to the jaw.

This may not look like a poem, but it is. Read
it aloud and you will discover the rhymes.

Football
by Walt Mason

The Game was ended, and the noise at last had
died away, and now they gathered up the boys where
they in pieces lay. And one was hammered in the
ground by many a jolt and jar; some fragments never
have been found, they flew away so far. They found a
stack of tawny hair, some fourteen cubits high; it
was the half-back, lying there, where he had crawled
to die. They placed the pieces on a door, and from
the crimson field, that hero then they gently bore,
like soldier on his shield. The surgeon toiled the
livelong night above the gory wreck; he got the ribs
adjusted right, the wishbone and the neck. He
soldered on the ears and toes, and got the spine in
place, and fixed a gutta-percha nose upon the
mangled face. And then he washed his hands and said:
"I'm glad that task is done!" The half-back raised
his fractured head, and cried: "I call this fun!"

Thunder Butte

from *When Thunders Spoke*
by Virginia Driving Hawk Sneve

Fifteen-year-old Norman Two Bull is a modern Sioux
boy who does not accept the old Indian beliefs. One
night he goes to his grandfather's tent, which is near
Norman's house on the Sioux reservation. Old Matt
Two Bull tells him that he has dreamed that if
Norman would go to the top of the Butte of
Thunders—known to the Sioux as a *Wakan*, or holy
hill—good things will happen. But Norman must
follow the old way—up the south side and down the
west side. When Norman agrees, his grandfather
gives him a strong willow cane to use as a probe and a
weapon. Early the next morning, Norman sets out.
After a difficult climb, he finally reaches the top of
the butte.

Norman gazed at a new world. The sun bathed the eastern valley in pale yellow which was spotted with dark clumps of sage. The creek was a green and silver serpent winding its way to the southeast. His grandfather's tent was a white shoe box in its clearing, and beside it stood a diminutive form waving a red flag. It was Matt Two Bull signaling with his shirt, and Norman knew that his grandfather had been watching him climb. He waved his hat in reply and then walked to the outer edge of the butte.[1]

The summit was not as smoothly flat as it looked from below. Norman stepped warily over the many cracks and holes that pitted the surface. He was elated that he had successfully made the difficult ascent, but now as he surveyed the butte top he had a sense of discomfort.

There were burn scars on the rough summit, and Norman wondered if these spots were where the lightning had struck, or were they evidence of ancient man-made fires? He remembered that this was a sacred place to the old ones and his uneasiness increased. He longed to be back on the secure level of the plains.

On the west edge he saw that the butte cast a sharp shadow below because the rim protruded as sharply as it had on the slope he'd climbed. Two flat rocks jutted up on either side of a narrow opening, and Norman saw shallow steps hewn into the space between. This must be the trail of which his grandfather had spoken.

Norman stepped down and then quickly turned to hug the butte face as the steps ended abruptly in space. The rest of the rocky staircase lay broken and crumbled below. The only way down was to jump.

He cautiously let go of the willow branch and

---

1. A butte is a steep, flat-topped hill that stands alone. Many buttes rise six hundred feet (180 meters) above the surrounding plains.

watched how it landed and bounced against the rocks. He took a deep breath as if to draw courage from the air. He lowered himself so that he was hanging by his fingertips to the last rough step, closed his eyes and dropped.

The impact of his landing stung the soles of his feet. He stumbled and felt the cut of the sharp rocks against one knee as he struggled to retain his balance. He did not fall and finally stood upright breathing deeply until the wild pounding of his heart slowed. "Wow," he said softly as he looked back up at the ledge, "that must have been at least a twenty-foot drop."

He picked up the willow branch and started walking slowly down the steep slope. The trail Matt Two Bull had told him about had been obliterated by years of falling rock. Loose shale and gravel shifted under Norman's feet, and he probed cautiously ahead with the cane to test the firmness of each step.

He soon found stones which he thought were agates. He identified them by spitting on each rock and rubbing the wet spot with his finger. The dull rock seemed to come alive! Variegated hues of brown and gray glowed as if polished. They were agates all right. Quickly he had his salt bag half full.

It was almost noon and his stomach growled. He stopped to rest against a large boulder and pulled out his lunch from his shirt. But his mouth was too dry to chew the cheese sandwich. He couldn't swallow without water.

Thirsty and hungry, Norman decided to go straight down the butte and head for home.

Walking more confidently as the slope leveled out he thrust the pointed cane carelessly into the ground. He suddenly fell as the cane went deep into the soft shale.

Norman slid several feet. Loose rocks rolled around him as he came to rest against a boulder. He lay still for a long time fearing that his tumble might cause a rock fall. But no thundering slide came, so he cautiously climbed back to where the tip of the willow branch protruded from the ground.

He was afraid that the cane may have plunged into a rattlesnake den. Carefully he pulled out the stout branch, wiggling it this way and that with one hand while he dug with the other. It came loose, sending a shower of rocks down the hill, and Norman saw that something else was sticking up in the hole he had uncovered.

Curious, and seeing no sign of snakes, he kept digging and soon found the tip of a leather-covered stick. Bits of leather and wood fell off in his hand as he gently pulled. The stick, almost as long as he was tall and curved on one end, emerged as he tugged. Holding it before him, his heart pounding with excitement, he realized that he had found a thing that once belonged to the old ones.

Norman shivered at the thought that he may have disturbed a grave, which was *tehinda*, forbidden. He

cleared more dirt away but saw no bones nor other sign that this was a burial place. Quickly he picked up the stick and his willow cane and hurried down the hill. When he reached the bottom he discovered that in his fall the salt bag of agates had pulled loose from his belt. But he did not return to search for it. It would take most of the afternoon to travel around the base of the butte to the east side.

The creek was in the deep shade of the butte when he reached it and thirstily flopped down and drank. He crossed the shallow stream and walked to his grandfather's tent.

"You have been gone a long time," Matt Two Bull greeted as Norman walked into the clearing where the old man was seated.

"I have come from the west side of the butte, Grandpa," Norman said wearily. He sat down on the ground and examined a tear in his jeans and the bruise on his knee.

"Was it difficult?" the old man asked.

"Yes," Norman nodded. He told of the rough climb up the south slope, the jump down and finally of his fall which led him to discover the long leather-covered stick. He held the stick out to his grandfather who took it and examined it carefully.

"Are you sure there was no body in the place where you found this?"

Norman shook his head. "No, I found nothing else but the stick. Do you know what it is, Grandpa?"

"You have found a *coup* stick which belonged to the old ones."

"I know that it is old because the wood is brittle and the leather is peeling, but what is—was a *coup* stick?" Norman asked.

"In the days when the old ones roamed all of the plains," the old man swept his hand in a circle, "a courageous act of valor was thought to be more

important than killing an enemy. When a warrior rode
or ran up to his enemy, close enough to touch the man
with a stick, without killing or being killed, the action
was called *coup*.

"The French, the first white men in this part of the
land, named this brave deed *coup*. In their language
the word meant 'hit' or 'strike.' The special stick which

was used to strike with came to be known as a *coup* stick.

"Some sticks were long like this one," Matt Two Bull held the stick upright. "Some were straight, and others had a curve on the end like the sheep herder's crook," he pointed to the curving end of the stick.

"The sticks were decorated with fur or painted leather strips. A warrior kept count of his *coups* by tying an eagle feather to the crook for each brave deed. See," he pointed to the staff end, "here is a remnant of a tie thong which must have once held a feather."

The old man and boy closely examined the *coup* stick. Matt Two Bull traced with his finger the faint zig zag design painted on the stick. "See," he said, "it is the thunderbolt."

"What does that mean?" Norman asked.

"The Thunders favored a certain few of the young men who sought their vision on the butte. The thunderbolt may have been part of a sacred dream sent as a token of the Thunders' favor. If this was so, the young man could use the thunderbolt symbol on his possessions."

"How do you suppose the stick came to be on the butte?" Norman asked.

His grandfather shook his head. "No one can say. Usually such a thing was buried with a dead warrior as were his weapons and other prized belongings."

"Is the *coup* stick what you dreamed about, Grandpa?"

"No. In my dream I only knew that you were to find a *Wakan*, a holy thing. But I did not know what it would be."

Norman laughed nervously. "What do you mean, *Wakan?* Is this stick haunted?"

Matt Two Bull smiled, "No, not like you mean in a fearful way. But in a sacred manner because it once had great meaning to the old ones."

"But why should I have been the one to find it?" Norman questioned.

His grandfather shrugged, "Perhaps to help you understand the ways—the values of the old ones."

"But nobody believes in that kind of thing anymore," Norman scoffed. "And even if people did, I couldn't run out and hit my enemy with the stick and get away with it." He smiled thinking of Mr. Brannon. "No one would think I was brave. I'd probably just get thrown in jail."

Suddenly Norman felt compelled to stop talking. In the distance he heard a gentle rumble which seemed to come from the butte. He glanced up at the hill looming high above and saw that it was capped with dark, low-hanging clouds.

Matt Two Bull looked too and smiled. "The Thunders are displeased with your thoughts," he said to Norman. "Listen to their message."

A sharp streak of lightning split the clouds and the thunder cracked and echoed over the plains.

Norman was frightened but he answered with bravado, "The message I get is that a storm is coming," but his voice betrayed him by quavering. "Maybe you'd better come home with me, Grandpa. Your tent will be soaked through if it rains hard."

"No," murmured Matt Two Bull, "no rain will come. It is just the Thunders speaking." There was another spark of lightning, and an explosive reverberation sounded as if in agreement with the old man.

Norman jumped to his feet. "Well, I'm going home. Mom will be worried because I'm late now." He turned to leave.

"Wait!" Matt Two Bull commanded. "Take the *coup* stick with you."

Norman backed away, "No, I don't want it. You can have it."

The old man rose swiftly despite the stiffness of his

years and sternly held out the stick to the boy. "You found it. It belongs to you. Take it!"

Norman slowly reached out his hands and took the stick.

"Even if you think the old ways are only superstition and the stick no longer has meaning, it is all that remains of an old life and must be treated with respect." Matt Two Bull smiled at the boy. "Take it," he repeated gently, "and hang it in the house where it will not be handled."

Norman hurried home as fast as he could carrying the long stick in one hand and the willow cane in the other. He felt vaguely uneasy and somehow a little frightened. It was only when he reached the security of his home that he realized the thunder had stopped and there had been no storm.

"Mom," he called as he went into the house, "I'm home."

His mother was standing at the stove. "Oh, Norman," she greeted him smiling. "I'm glad you're back. I was beginning to worry." Her welcoming smile turned to a frown as she saw the *coup* stick in Norman's hand. "What is that?"

"Grandpa says it's a *coup* stick. Here," Norman handed it to her, "take a look at it. It's interesting the way it is made and decor—"

"No," Sarah interrupted and backed away from him. "I won't touch that heathen thing no matter what it is! Get it out of the house!"

"What?" Norman asked, surprised and puzzled. "There is nothing wrong with it. It's just an old stick I found up on the butte."

"I don't care," Sarah insisted. "I won't have such a thing in the house!"

"But, Mom," Norman protested, "it's not like we believe in those old ways the way Grandpa does."

But Sarah was adamant. "Take it out of the house!"

she ordered, pointing to the door. "We'll talk about it
when your dad gets home."

Reluctantly Norman took the *coup* stick outside and
gently propped it against the house and sat on the
steps to wait for his father. He was confused. First by
his grandfather's reverent treatment of the *coup* stick
as if it were a sacred object and then by Sarah's
rejection of it as a heathen symbol.

He looked at the stick where it leaned against the
wall and shook his head. So much fuss over a brittle,
rotten length of wood. Even though he had gone
through a lot of hard, even dangerous, effort to get it
he was now tempted to heave it out on the trash pile.

Norman wearily leaned his head against the house.
He suddenly felt tired and his knee ached. As he sat
wearily rubbing the bruise John Two Bull rode the old
mare into the yard. Norman got up and walked back to
the shed to help unsaddle the horse.

John climbed stiffly out of the saddle. His faded
blue work shirt and jeans were stained with
perspiration and dirt. His boots were worn and
scuffed.

"Hard day, Dad?" Norman asked.

"Yeah," John answered, slipping the bridle over the mare's head. "Rustlers got away with twenty steers last night. I spent the day counting head and mending fences. Whoever the thief was cut the fence, drove a truck right onto the range and loaded the cattle without being seen." He began rubbing the mare down as she munched the hay in her manger.

"How did your day on the butte go?" John asked.

"Rough," Norman answered. "I'm beat too. The climb up the butte was tough and coming down was bad too." He told his father all that had happened on the butte, winding up with the climax of his falling and finding the old *coup* stick.

John listened attentively and did not interrupt until Norman told of Matt Two Bull's reaction to the stick. "I think Grandpa's mind has gotten weak," Norman said. "He really believes that the *coup* stick has some sort of mysterious power and that the Thunders were talking."

"Don't make fun of your grandfather," John reprimanded, "or of the old ways he believes in."

"Okay, okay," Norman said quickly, not wanting another scolding. "But Mom is just the opposite from Grandpa," he went on. "She doesn't want the *coup* stick in the house. Says it's heathen."

He walked to the house and handed the stick to his father. John examined it and then carried it into the house.

"John!" Sarah exclaimed as she saw her husband bring the stick into the room. "I told Norman, and I tell you, that I won't have that heathenish thing in the house!"

But John ignored her and propped the stick against the door while he pulled his tool box out from under the washstand to look for a hammer and nails.

"John," Sarah persisted, "did you hear me?"

"I heard," John answered quietly, but Norman knew

his father was angry. "And I don't want to hear anymore."

Norman was surprised to hear his father speak in such a fashion. John was slow to anger, usually spoke quietly and tried to avoid conflict of any kind, but now he went on.

"This," he said holding the *coup* stick upright, "is a relic of our people's past glory when it was a good thing to be an Indian. It is a symbol of something that shall never be again."

Sarah gasped and stepped in front of her husband as he started to climb a chair to pound the nails in the wall above the window. "But that's what I mean," she said. "Those old ways were just superstition. They don't mean anything now—they can't because such a way of life can't be anymore. We don't need to have those old symbols of heathen ways hanging in the house!" She grabbed at the *coup* stick, but John jerked it out of her reach.

"Don't touch it!" he shouted and Sarah fell back against the table in shocked surprise. Norman took a step forward as if to protect his mother. The boy had never seen his father so angry.

John shook his head as if to clear it. "Sarah, I'm sorry. I didn't mean to yell. It's just that the old ones would not permit a woman to touch such a thing as this." He handed Norman the stick to hold while he hammered the nails in the wall. Then he hung the stick above the window.

"Sarah," he said as he put the tools away, "think of the stick as an object that could be in a museum, a part of history. It's not like we were going to fall down on our knees and pray to it." His voice was light and teasing as he tried to make peace.

But Sarah stood stiffly at the stove preparing supper and would not answer. Norman felt sick. His appetite was gone. When his mother set a plate of food before him he excused himself saying, "I guess I'm too tired to eat," and went to his room.

But after he had undressed and crawled into bed he couldn't sleep. His mind whirled with the angry words his parents had spoken. They had never argued in such a way before. "I wish I had never brought that old stick home," he whispered and then pulled the pillow over his head to shut out the sound of the low rumble of thunder that came from the west.

Old Matt Two Bull dreamed of good things happening if Norman climbed the butte. But the first thing the old *coup* stick brings is a family argument. You can find out what happens next by reading *When Thunders Spoke*. The author, Virginia Driving Hawk Sneve, who spent her childhood on a Sioux reservation, has written other books about the American Indians, including *Betrayed*, *High Elk's Treasure*, and *Jimmy Yellow Hawk*.

Why the Kangaroo Hops on Two Legs

an adaptation of "Bohra the Kangaroo" from
Australian Legendary Tales by K. Langloh Parker

Long, long ago—in the time the Australian Aborigines
call the Dreamtime—Bohra, the kangaroo, did not hop
on two legs as he does today. Instead, he walked on
four legs, like a dog. And he had four long, pointed
teeth, just as dogs do.

One bright, starry night, as Bohra was nibbling on
grass and tender leaves, he heard the sound of singing.
Looking up, he saw the red glow of many campfires
twinkling through the darkness. Filled with curiosity,
Bohra crept closer. When he drew near, he saw that
the fires were arranged in a circle. Within the circle of
fires, men were dancing. Their dark bodies were
decorated with red and white designs. Stuck to some of
the painted designs were tufts of fuzzy down from
birds such as Gooloo, the magpie. Women sat outside
the circle of fires, singing in clear voices. As they
sang, they clicked clapsticks together and thumped on
rolled-up possum skins. The people were holding a
corroboree, or sacred ceremony.

Round and round went the dancing men. Faster and
faster went the *click-click-click* of the clapsticks.

Louder and louder went the *thump-thumpah-thump* on the possum skins. The fires flickered in the darkness. Overhead, the stars sparkled and the Milky Way stretched across the sky like a bright, glowing river.

As Bohra watched, he grew more and more interested. The clicking and thumping excited him. The singing and dancing thrilled him. He felt that he, too, wanted to dance—just as the men were dancing. Suddenly, standing up on his hind legs so that he would look like the men, he jumped into the circle of fires! Balancing himself with his tail, he began to hop behind the dancers.

At the sight of him, the women stopped singing and began to shriek and point. The men stopped dancing and looked to see what the trouble was. When they saw Bohra standing on his hind legs trying to imitate them, some were angry. "Kill him!" they shouted. But others said, "No, no. Let us see him dance."

The women were told to start their singing again, to beat the possum skins and click their clapsticks. As they did so, the men began to dance. And after them, at the end of the line, came Bohra. He was hopping on two legs and trying to do what the men did.

As the men danced, they turned their heads to watch Bohra. Soon they began to grin and chuckle. Bohra looked very funny hopping around so seriously, a timid expression on his face, and his tail leaving a snakelike track behind him. Finally, the men were laughing so hard they had to stop dancing.

Then, one of the men had an idea. He led the others out of the circle and into the surrounding darkness. There he had them gather bundles of long grass. He told them what he wanted them to do, and the men quickly went to work.

After a time, the men called to the women to pile more wood on the fires and start their singing. As the fires rose higher and higher, the women clicked their clapsticks, thumped on the possum skins, and raised their voices in song. Then the line of painted men came back into the circle of fires. But now, hanging from the backs of their belts were long, crude tails of woven grass.

The men began to dance the way Bohra danced. They hopped round the ring as Bohra did, their grass tails waggling behind them. They held their arms up in front of them, with their hands dangling down, the way Bohra held his forepaws as he danced. The men looked so funny the women could hardly manage to sing.

At last, with a great "Hooh! Hooh! Hooh!" from the dancers, the singing and clicking and thumping faded into silence. The tired dancers sank to the ground. It was nearly dawn. Already the laughing cries of the kookaburra birds could be heard.

After a few moments, an old wirinun, or magician, stood up. "This Bohra came to our corroboree without

being invited. He must be shown that he has no right to do this," said the wirinun. "But, we will not kill him, for he has shown us a new dance. Instead, from now on, he and all his tribe shall hop on their hind legs, using their tails to balance themselves—just as he hopped when he was dancing. And they shall hold their forepaws up in front of them, just as he did." Motioning to the others to follow him, he said, "Now, let us make this Bohra one of us. He and his tribe shall be our brothers. Then, if any of them see our corroborees, they will not tell others what they have seen."

The men took Bohra into the trees, away from the fires and the women. There they performed the ceremony that made him a member of their tribe. It was the same ceremony that their young boys went through when they came of age. As part of the ceremony, the wirinun took a boomerang and knocked out Bohra's long, pointed teeth.

From that day to this, no kangaroo has had these long, pointed teeth. And to this very day, every kangaroo hops on two legs, the way Bohra did that night when he joined the corroboree. And ever since that time, when the people of the Bohra tribe have a corroboree, they put on tails made of woven grass. Then they dance the kangaroo dance—just as Bohra danced it on that starry night in the long-ago Dreamtime.

There are many, many wonderful "why" stories. If you haven't read them, try "How the Camel Got His Hump" and *Why Mosquitoes Buzz in People's Ears*, both in Volume 1 of *Childcraft*. Or get the book, *Tales of the Nimipoo* by Eleanor Heady, which has twenty "why" stories with Coyote, the American Indian trickster, as the hero.

Eletelephony
by Laura E. Richards

Once there was an elephant,
Who tried to use the telephant—
No! no! I mean an elephone
Who tried to use the telephone—
(Dear me! I am not certain quite
That even now I've got it right.)

Howe'er it was, he got his trunk
Entangled in the telephunk;
The more he tried to get it free,
The louder buzzed the telephee—
(I fear I'd better drop the song
Of elephop and telephong!)

What Is It?
author unknown

The beginning of eternity,
The end of time and space,
The beginning of every end,
The end of every place.

The letter e

Banananananananana
by William Cole

I thought I'd win the spelling bee
    And get right to the top,
But I started to spell "banana,"
    And I didn't know when to stop.

The Ptarmigan
author unknown

The ptarmigan is strange,
As strange as he can be;
Never sits on ptelephone poles
Or roosts upon a ptree.
And the way he ptakes pto spelling
Is the strangest thing pto me.

The Bremen Town Musicians

adapted from *Grimm's Fairy Tales*
by Jakob and Wilhelm Grimm

Jakob and Wilhelm Grimm were born in Germany just
about two hundred years ago. Their collection of fairy
tales, or "Household Tales" as they called them, have
been favorites for generations. You'll see why when
you read this one.

❧ ❧ ❧

A certain man had a donkey that had carried the corn
sacks to the mill untiringly for many years. But his
strength was going, and he was growing more and
more unfit for work. Then his master began to think
that the donkey wasn't worth his hay. But the donkey,
seeing the harm that might come to him, ran away
and started out on the road to Bremen. "There," he
thought, "I can surely be a town musician."

When he had walked some distance, he found a
hound lying in the road, panting like one who had run
till he was tired. "What are you panting so for, you big
fellow?" asked the donkey.

"Ah," replied the hound, "as I am old and grow
weaker every day and can hunt no more, my master
wanted to kill me. So I ran away. But now how am I to
earn my food?"

"I'll tell you what," said the donkey, "I am going to
Bremen and shall be a town musician there. Come with
me and become a musician also."

The hound agreed, and on they went.

Before long they came to a cat sitting in the road,
with a face as sad as three rainy days! "Now then, old
one, what has gone wrong with you?" asked the
donkey.

"Who can be merry when his life is in danger?" answered the cat. "I am now getting old. My teeth are worn to stumps. I prefer to sit by the fire and sleep rather than hunt about after mice. So my mistress wanted to drown me. That's why I ran away. But now what am I to do? Where am I to go?"

"Come with us to Bremen. You understand night music, so you can be a town musician."

The cat thought it was a good idea and went with them. After this the three of them came to a farmyard where a cock was sitting upon the gate, crowing with all his might. "Your crowing chills my bones," said the donkey. "What is the matter?"

"I have been predicting fine weather because it is the day on which the housewife washes her child's little shirts and wants to dry them," said the cock. "But guests are coming for Sunday, so the housewife has no pity and has told the cook that she intends to eat me in the soup tomorrow. And this evening I am to have my head cut off. Now I am crowing loudly while I can."

"Ah, cock," said the donkey, "you had better come away with us. We are going to Bremen. You can find something better than death there. You have a good

voice, and if we make music together it must have some quality!"

The cock agreed to this plan, and all four went on together. But they could not reach the city of Bremen in one day. In the evening they came to a forest where they decided to spend the night. The donkey and the hound lay down under a large tree, while the cat and the cock settled themselves in the branches. But the cock flew right to the top where he would be the safest of all. Before he went to sleep, he looked all around and thought he saw in the distance a little spark of light burning. He called out to his companions that there must be a house not far off, for he saw a light. The donkey said, "If so, we had better get up and go on, for the shelter here is bad." The hound thought that a few bones with some meat on them would do him good, too!

So they made their way to the place where the light was and soon saw it shine brighter and grow larger until they came to a well-lighted robber's house. The donkey, as he was the biggest, went to the window and looked in.

"What do you see, my donkey?" asked the cock.

"What do I see?" answered the donkey. "I see a table covered with good things to eat and drink, and robbers sitting at it enjoying themselves."

"That would be the sort of thing for us," said the cock.

"Yes, yes. Ah, how I wish we were there!" said the donkey.

Then the animals talked together of how they might drive away the robbers. At last they thought of a plan. The donkey was to place himself with his forefeet upon the window ledge, the hound was to jump on the donkey's back, the cat was to climb upon the dog, and lastly the cock was to fly up and perch upon the head of the cat.

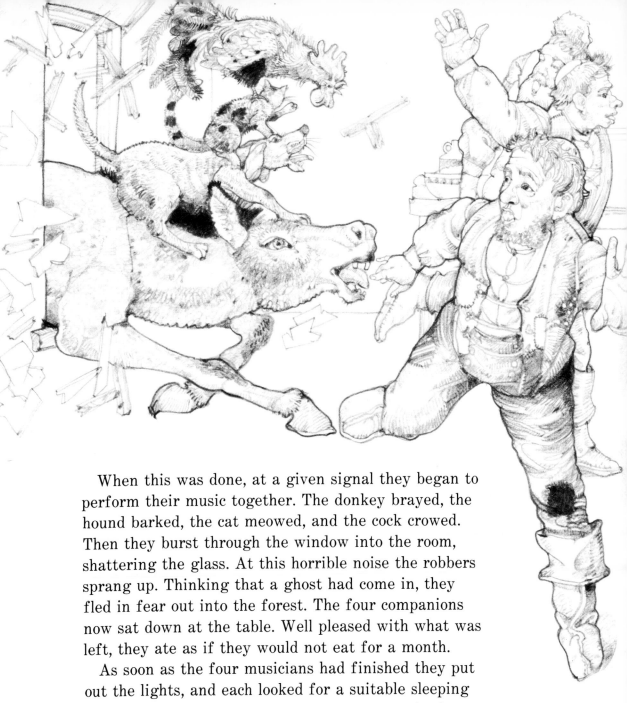

When this was done, at a given signal they began to perform their music together. The donkey brayed, the hound barked, the cat meowed, and the cock crowed. Then they burst through the window into the room, shattering the glass. At this horrible noise the robbers sprang up. Thinking that a ghost had come in, they fled in fear out into the forest. The four companions now sat down at the table. Well pleased with what was left, they ate as if they would not eat for a month.

As soon as the four musicians had finished they put out the lights, and each looked for a suitable sleeping place. The donkey lay down upon some straw in the yard, the hound behind the door, the cat upon the hearth near the warm ashes, and the cock perched himself upon a beam of the roof. And, being tired with their long walk, they soon went to sleep.

When it was past midnight, and the robbers saw from afar that the light was no longer burning in their house and that all appeared quiet, the leader said, "We shouldn't have let ourselves be frightened so." And he ordered one of them to go and inspect the house.

So one of them went and, finding all still, went into the kitchen to light a candle. Taking the shining, fiery eyes of the cat for live coals, he held a match to them to light it. But the cat did not understand the action and flew in his face, spitting and scratching. The robber was so frightened that he ran to the back door. But the dog, who lay there, sprang up and bit his leg. And as he ran across the yard by the pile of straw, the donkey gave him a hard kick with its hind foot. And the cock, who had been awakened by the noise and was very excited, cried down from the beam, "Cock-a-doodle-doo!"

Then the robber ran back as fast as he could to his leader and said, "Ah, there is a horrible witch sitting in the house. She spat on me and scratched my face with her long nails. And by the door stands a man with a knife who stabbed me in the leg. And in the yard there lies a black monster who beat me with a wooden club. And above, upon the roof, sits a judge who called out, 'Bring the villain here to me!' So I got away as fast as I could."

After this the robbers did not dare to go into the house again. But it suited the four Bremen town musicians so well that they did not care to leave it any more.

Altogether, the Brothers Grimm collected 210 tales. Among these are such favorites as "The Shoemaker and the Elves" (which is in Volume 1 of *Childcraft*), "Rumpelstiltskin," "Rapunzel," and "Hansel and Gretel." Many of the tales are published in attractive individual editions.

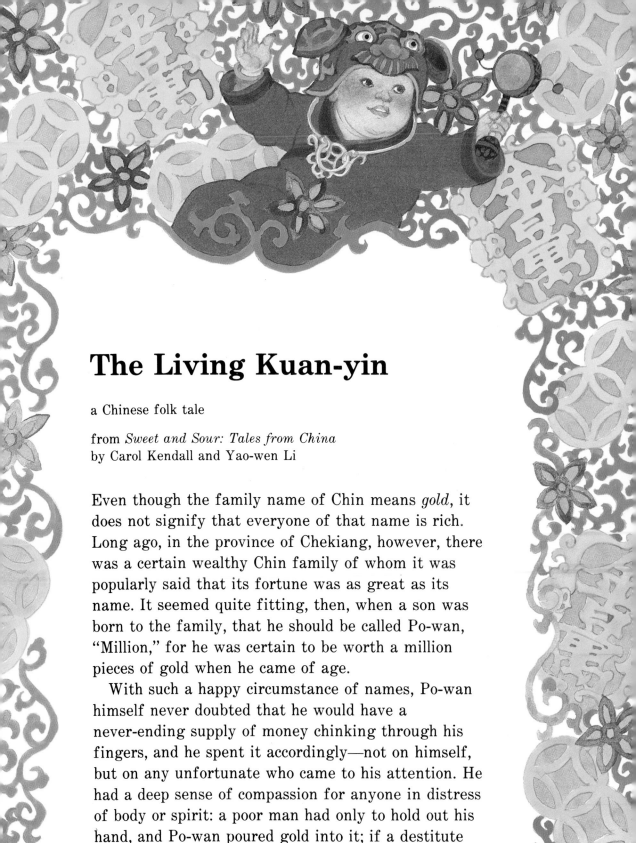

The Living Kuan-yin

a Chinese folk tale

from *Sweet and Sour: Tales from China*
by Carol Kendall and Yao-wen Li

Even though the family name of Chin means *gold*, it
does not signify that everyone of that name is rich.
Long ago, in the province of Chekiang, however, there
was a certain wealthy Chin family of whom it was
popularly said that its fortune was as great as its
name. It seemed quite fitting, then, when a son was
born to the family, that he should be called Po-wan,
"Million," for he was certain to be worth a million
pieces of gold when he came of age.

With such a happy circumstance of names, Po-wan
himself never doubted that he would have a
never-ending supply of money chinking through his
fingers, and he spent it accordingly—not on himself,
but on any unfortunate who came to his attention. He
had a deep sense of compassion for anyone in distress
of body or spirit: a poor man had only to hold out his
hand, and Po-wan poured gold into it; if a destitute

widow and her brood of starvelings but lifted
sorrowful eyes to his, he provided them with food and
lodging and friendship for the rest of their days.

In such wise did he live that even a million gold
pieces were not enough to support him. His resources
so dwindled that finally he scarcely had enough food
for himself; his clothes flapped threadbare on his
wasted frame; and the cold seeped into his bone
marrow for lack of a fire. Still he gave away the little
money that came to him.

One day, as he scraped out half of his bowl of rice
for a beggar even hungrier than he, he began to
ponder on his destitute state.

"Why am I so poor?" he wondered. "I have never
spent extravagantly. I have never, from the day of my
birth, done an evil deed. Why then am I, whose very
name is A Million Pieces of Gold, no longer able to
find even a copper to give this unfortunate creature,
and have only a bowl of rice to share with him?"

He thought long about his situation and at last
determined to go without delay to the South Sea.
Therein, it was told, dwelt the all-merciful goddess, the
Living Kuan-yin, who could tell the past and future.
He would put his question to her and she would tell
him the answer.

Soon he had left his home country behind and
travelled for many weeks in unfamiliar lands. One day
he found his way barred by a wide and furiously
flowing river. As he stood first on one foot and then
on the other, wondering how he could possibly get
across, he heard a commanding voice calling from the
top of an overhanging cliff.

"Chin Po-wan!" the voice said, "if you are going to
the South Sea, please ask the Living Kuan-yin a
question for me!"

"Yes, yes, of course," Po-wan agreed at once, for he
had never in his life refused a request made of him. In

any case, the Living Kuan-yin permitted each person
who approached her three questions, and he had but
one of his own to ask.

Craning his head towards the voice coming from
above, he suddenly began to tremble, for the speaker
was a gigantic snake with a body as large as a temple
column. Po-wan was glad he had agreed so readily to
the request.

"Ask her then," said the snake, "why I am not yet a
dragon even though I have practiced self-denial for
more than one thousand years?"

"That I will do, and gl-gladly," stammered Po-wan,
hoping that the snake would continue to practice
self-denial just a bit longer. "But, your ... your
Snakery ... or your Serpentry, perhaps I should say ...
that is ... you see, don't you ... first I must cross this
raging river, and I know not how."

"That is no problem, at all," said the snake. "I shall
carry you across, of course."

"Of course," Po-wan echoed weakly. Overcoming his fear and his reluctance to touch the slippery-slithery scales, Chin Po-wan climbed on to the snake's back and rode across quite safely. Politely, and just a bit hurriedly, he thanked the self-denying serpent and bade him goodbye. Then he continued on his way to the South Sea.

By noon he was very hungry. Fortunately a nearby inn offered meals at a price he could afford. While waiting for his bowl of rice, he chatted with the innkeeper and told him of the Snake of the Cliff, which the innkeeper knew well and respected, for the serpent always denied bandits the crossing of the river. Inadvertently, during the exchange of stories, Po-wan revealed the purpose of his journey.

"Why then," cried the innkeeper, "let me prevail upon your generosity to ask a word for me." He laid an appealing hand on Po-wan's ragged sleeve. "I have a beautiful daughter," he said, "wonderfully amiable and pleasing of disposition. But although she is in her twentieth year, she has never in all her life uttered a single word. I should be very much obliged if you would ask the Living Kuan-yin why she is unable to speak."

Po-wan, much moved by the innkeeper's plea for his mute daughter, of course promised to do so. For after all, the Living Kuan-yin allowed each person three questions and he had but one of his own to ask.

Nightfall found him far from any inn, but there were houses in the neighbourhood, and he asked for lodging at the largest. The owner, a man obviously of great wealth, was pleased to offer him a bed in a fine chamber, but first begged him to partake of a hot meal and good drink. Po-wan ate well, slept soundly, and, much refreshed, was about to depart the following morning, when his good host, having learned that Po-wan was journeying to the South Sea, asked if he would be kind enough to put a question for him to the Living Kuan-yin.

"For twenty years," he said, "from the time this house was built, my garden has been cultivated with the utmost care, yet in all those years, not one tree, not one small plant, has bloomed or borne fruit, and because of this, no bird comes to sing nor bee to gather nectar. I don't like to put you to a bother, Chin Po-wan, but as you are going to the South Sea anyway, perhaps you would not mind seeking out the Living Kuan-yin and asking her why the plants in my garden don't bloom?"

"I shall be delighted to put the question to her," said Po-wan. For after all, the Living Kuan-yin allowed each person three questions, and he had but . . .

Travelling onward, Po-wan examined the quandary in which he found himself. The Living Kuan-yin allowed but three questions, and he had somehow, without quite knowing how, accumulated four questions. One of them, would have to go unasked, but which? If he left out his own question, his whole journey would have been in vain. If, on the other hand, he left out the question of the snake, or the innkeeper, or the kind host, he would break his promise and betray their faith in him.

"A promise should never be made if it cannot be kept," he told himself. "I made the promises and therefore I must keep them. Besides, the journey will not be in vain, for at least some of these problems will be solved by the Living Kuan-yin. Furthermore, assisting others must certainly be counted as a good deed, and the more good deeds abroad in the land, the better for everyone, including me."

At last he came into the presence of the Living Kuan-yin.

First, he asked the serpent's question: "Why is the Snake of the Cliff not yet a dragon, although he has

practised self-denial for more than one thousand
years?"

And the Kuan-yin answered: "On his head are seven
bright pearls. If he removes six of them, he can
become a dragon."

Next, Po-wan asked the innkeeper's question: "Why
is the innkeeper's daughter unable to speak, although
she is in the twentieth year of her life?"

And the Living Kuan-yin answered: "It is her fate
to remain mute until she sees the man destined to be
her husband."

Last, Po-wan asked the kind host's question: "Why
are there never blossoms in the rich man's garden,
although it has been carefully cultivated for twenty
years?"

And the Living Kuan-yin answered: "Buried in the garden are seven big jars filled with silver and gold. The flowers will bloom if the owner will rid himself of half the treasure."

Then Chin Po-wan thanked the Living Kuan-yin and bade her good-bye.

On his return journey, he stopped first at the rich man's house to give him the Living Kuan-yin's answer. In gratitude the rich man gave him half the buried treasure.

Next Po-wan went to the inn. As he approached, the innkeeper's daughter saw him from the window and called, "Chin Po-wan! Back already! What did the Living Kuan-yin say?"

Upon hearing his daughter speak at long last, the joyful innkeeper gave her in marriage to Chin Po-wan.

Lastly, Po-wan went to the cliffs by the furiously flowing river to tell the snake what the Living Kuan-yin had said. The grateful snake immediately gave him six of the bright pearls and promptly turned into a magnificent dragon, the remaining pearl in his forehead lighting the headland like a great beacon.

And so it was that Chin Po-wan, that generous and good man, was once more worth a million pieces of gold.

Did you like this tale? If so, there are many others like it waiting for you in *Sweet and Sour: Tales from China*, which is a choice collection of charming Chinese folk tales. And if you look in the folklore section of your library, you will find hundreds of other books filled with tales from many lands.

The Emperor's New Clothes

by Hans Christian Andersen

Hans Christian Andersen died more than a hundred
years ago, but his many wonderful stories continue to
live in the hearts of readers. Most are fairy tales
created in his own mind, but some, like this one, are
imaginative retellings of folk tales.

Many years ago there was an Emperor who was so
excessively fond of new clothes that he spent all his
money on them. He cared nothing about his soldiers or
for the theater, or for driving in the woods, except for
the sake of showing off his new clothes. He had a
costume for every hour in the day. Instead of saying,
as one does about any other King or Emperor, "He is
in his council chamber," the people here always said,
"The Emperor is in his dressing room."

Life was very gay in the great town where he lived.
Hosts of strangers came to visit it, and among them
one day were two swindlers. They gave themselves out

as weavers and said that they knew how to weave the most beautiful fabrics imaginable. Not only were the colors and patterns unusually fine, but the clothes that were made of this cloth had a peculiar quality of becoming invisible to every person who was not fit for the office he held, or who was impossibly dull.

"Those must be splendid clothes," thought the Emperor. "By wearing them I should be able to discover which men in my kingdom are unfitted for their posts. I shall be able to tell the wise men from the fools. Yes, I certainly must order some of that stuff to be woven for me."

The Emperor paid the two swindlers a lot of money in advance, so that they might begin their work at once.

They did put up two looms and pretended to weave, but they had nothing whatever upon their shuttles. At the outset they asked for a quantity of the finest silk and the purest gold thread, all of which they put into their own bags while they worked away at the empty looms far into the night.

"I should like to know how those weavers are getting on with their cloth," thought the Emperor, but he felt a little queer when he reflected that anyone who was stupid or unfit for his post would not be able to see it. He certainly thought that he need have no fears for himself. Still he thought he would send somebody else first to see how the work was getting on. Everybody in the town knew what wonderful power the stuff possessed, and every one was anxious to see how stupid his neighbor was.

"I will send my faithful old minister to the weavers," thought the Emperor. "He will be best able to see how the stuff looks, for he is a clever man and no one fulfills his duties better than he does!"

So the good old minister went into the room where the two swindlers sat working at the empty loom.

"Heaven help us," thought the old minister, opening

his eyes very wide. "Why, I can't see a thing!" But he took care not to say so.

Both the swindlers begged him to be good enough to step a little nearer. They asked if he did not think it a good pattern and beautiful coloring, and they pointed to the empty loom. The poor old minister stared as hard as he could, but he could not see anything, for of course there was nothing to see.

"Good heavens!" thought he. "Is it possible that I am a fool? I have never thought so, and nobody must know it. Am I not fit for my post? It will never do to say that I cannot see the stuff."

"Well, sir, you don't say anything about the stuff," said the one who was pretending to weave.

"Oh, it is beautiful! Quite charming," said the minister, looking through his spectacles. "Such a pattern and such colors! I will certainly tell the Emperor that the stuff pleases me very much."

"We are delighted to hear you say so," said the swindlers, and then they named all the colors and described the peculiar pattern. The old minister paid close attention to what they said, so as to be able to repeat it when he got home to the Emperor.

Then the swindlers went on to demand more money, more silk, and more gold, to be able to proceed with the weaving. They put it all into their own pockets. Not a single strand was ever put into the loom. But they went on as before, pretending to weave at the empty loom.

The Emperor soon sent another faithful official to see how the stuff was getting on and if it would soon be ready. The same thing happened to him as to the minister. He looked and looked, but as there was only the empty loom, he could see nothing at all.

"Is not this a beautiful piece of stuff?" said both the swindlers, showing and explaining the beautiful pattern and colors which were not there to be seen.

"I know I am no fool," thought the man, "so it must be that I am unfit for my good post. It is very strange, but I must not let on." So he praised the stuff he did not see, and assured the swindlers of his delight in the beautiful colors and the originality of the design. "It is absolutely charming!" he said to the Emperor.

Everybody in the town was now talking about this splendid stuff, and the Emperor thought he would like to see it while it was still on the loom. So, accompanied by a number of selected courtiers, among whom were the two faithful officials who had already seen the imaginary stuff, he went to visit the crafty impostors. They were working away as hard as ever they could at the empty loom.

"It is magnificent!" said both the honest officials. "Only see, Your Majesty, what a design! What colors!" And they pointed to the empty loom, for they each thought the others could see the stuff.

"What!" thought the Emperor. "I see nothing at all. This is terrible! Am I a fool? Am I not fit to be Emperor? Why, nothing worse could happen to me!

"Oh, it is beautiful," said the Emperor. "It has my

highest approval." He nodded his satisfaction as he gazed at the empty loom. Nothing would induce him to say that he could not see anything.

The whole suite gazed and gazed, but saw nothing more than all the others. However, they all exclaimed with His Majesty, "It is very beautiful!" They advised him to wear a suit made of this wonderful cloth on the occasion of a great procession which was just about to take place. "Magnificent! Gorgeous! Excellent!" went from mouth to mouth. They were all equally delighted with it. The Emperor gave each of the weavers an order of knighthood to be worn in his buttonhole and the title of "Gentleman Weaver."

The swindlers sat up the whole night before the day on which the procession was to take place. They burned sixteen candles, so that people might see how anxious they were to get the Emperor's new clothes ready. They pretended to take the stuff off the loom. They cut it out in the air with a huge pair of scissors, and they stitched away with needles without any thread in them.

At last they said, "Now the Emperor's new clothes are ready."

The Emperor, with his grandest courtiers, went to them himself. Both the swindlers raised one arm in the air, as if they were holding something. They said, "See, these are the trousers. This is the coat. Here is the mantle," and so on. "They are as light as a spider's web. One might think one had nothing on, but that is the very beauty of it."

"Yes," said all the courtiers, but they could not see anything, for there was nothing to see.

"Will Your Imperial Majesty be graciously pleased to take off your clothes?" said the impostors. "Then we may put on the new ones, along here before the great mirror."

The Emperor took off all his clothes, and the

impostors pretended to give him one article of dress
after the other of the new clothes which they had
pretended to make. They pretended to fasten
something around his waist and to tie on something.
This was the train. The Emperor turned round and
round in front of the mirror.

"How well His Majesty looks in the new clothes!
How becoming they are!" cried all the people. "What a
design, and what colors! They are most gorgeous
robes!"

"The canopy is waiting outside which is to be carried
over Your Majesty in the procession," said the master
of ceremonies.

"Well, I am quite ready," said the Emperor. "Don't
the clothes fit well?" Then he turned round again in
front of the mirror, so that he should seem to be
looking at his grand things.

The chamberlains who were to carry the train
stooped and pretended to lift it from the ground with
both hands, and they walked along with their hands in
the air. They dared not let it appear that they could
not see anything.

Then the Emperor walked along in the procession under the gorgeous canopy, and everybody in the streets and at the windows exclaimed, "How beautiful the Emperor's new clothes are! What a splendid train! And they fit to perfection!" Nobody would let it appear that he could see nothing, for that would prove that he was not fit for his post, or else he was a fool. None of the Emperor's clothes had been so successful before.

"But he has nothing on," said a little child.

"Oh, listen to the innocent," said its father. And one person whispered to the other what the child had said. "He has nothing on—a child says he has nothing on!"

"But he has nothing on!" at last cried all the people.

The Emperor writhed, for he knew it was true. But he thought, "The procession must go on now." So he held himself stiffer than ever, and the chamberlains held up the invisible train.

Did you enjoy this tale? If so, you'll want to read some of Hans Christian Andersen's other stories. You might try "The Princess and the Pea," "The Ugly Duckling," "The Tinderbox," "Thumbelina," "The Fir Tree," or "The Steadfast Tin Soldier."

The Codfish
author unknown

The codfish lays ten thousand eggs,
　The homely hen lays one.
The codfish never cackles
　To tell you what she's done.
And so we scorn the codfish,
　While the humble hen we prize,
Which only goes to show you
　That it pays to advertise.

Bees
by Jack Prelutsky

Every bee
that
ever was
was
partly
sting
and partly
. . . buzz.

The Puffin
by Robert Williams Wood

Upon this cake of ice is perched
The paddle-footed Puffin;
To find his double we have searched,
But have discovered—Nuffin!

A Wee Little Worm
by James Whitcomb Riley

A wee little worm in a hickory-nut
　Sang, happy as he could be,
"O I live in the heart of the whole round world,
　And it all belongs to me!"

Anansi and the Plantains

from *Anansi the Spider Man*
by Philip M. Sherlock

Who was Anansi?

He was a man and he was a spider.

When things went well he was a man, but when he
was in great danger he became a spider, safe in his
web high up on the ceiling. That was why his friend
Mouse called him "Ceiling Thomas."

Anansi's home was in the villages and forests of
West Africa. From there long years ago thousands of
men and women came to the islands of the Caribbean.
They brought with them the stories that they loved,
the stories about clever Br'er Anansi, and his friends
Tiger and Crow and Moos-Moos and Kisander the cat.

Today the people of the islands still tell these stories
to each other. So, in some country village in Jamaica
when the sun goes down the children gather round an
old woman and listen to the stories of Anansi.

In the dim light they see the animals—Goat, Rat,
Crow, and the others—behaving like men and women.
They see how excited everyone becomes as soon as
Anansi appears. They laugh at the way in which he
tricks all the strong animals and gets the better of
those who are much bigger than himself. At last the
story comes to an end. The night and bedtime come.
But next day when the children see Ceiling Thomas
they know that he is more than a spider. They know
that he is Anansi, the spider man, and they do him no
harm.

It was market day, but Anansi had no money. He sat at the door of his cottage and watched Tiger and Kisander the cat, Dog and Goat, and a host of others hurrying to the market to buy and sell. He had nothing to sell, for he had not done any work in his field. Turtle had won the few coins that he had saved in the broken calabash that he kept hidden under his bed. How was he to find food for his wife Crooky and for the children? Above all, how was he to find food for himself?

Soon Crooky came to the door and spoke to him.

"You must go out now, Anansi, and find something for us to eat. We have nothing for lunch, nothing for dinner, and tomorrow is Sunday. What are we going to do without a scrap of food in the house?"

"I am going out to work for some food," said Anansi. "Do not worry. Every day you have seen me go with nothing and come home with something. You watch and see!"

Anansi walked about until noon and found nothing, so he lay down to sleep under the shade of a large mango tree. There he slept and waited until the sun began to go down. Then, in the cool of the evening, he set off for home. He walked slowly, for he was ashamed to be going home empty-handed. He was asking himself what he was to do, and where he would find food for the children, when he came face to face with his old friend Rat going home with a large bunch of plantains on his head. The bunch was so big and heavy that Brother Rat had to bend down almost to the earth to carry it.

Anansi's eyes shone when he saw the plantains, and he stopped to speak to his friend Rat.

"How are you, my friend Rat? I haven't seen you for a very long time."

"Oh, I am staggering along, staggering along," said Rat. "And how are you—and the family?"

Anansi put on his longest face, so long that his chin almost touched his toes. He groaned and shook his head. "Ah, Brother Rat," he said, "times are hard, times are very hard. I can hardly find a thing to eat from one day to the next." At this tears came into his eyes, and he went on:

"I walked all yesterday. I have been walking all today and I haven't found a yam or a plantain." He glanced for a moment at the large bunch of plantains. "Ah, Br'er Rat, the children will have nothing but water for supper tonight."

"I am sorry to hear that," said Rat, "very sorry indeed. I know how I would feel if I had to go home to my wife and children without any food."

"Without even a plantain," said Anansi, and again he looked for a moment at the plantains.

Br'er Rat looked at the bunch of plantains, too. He put it on the ground and looked at it in silence.

Anansi said nothing, but he moved toward the plantains. They drew him like a magnet. He could not take his eyes away from them, except for an occasional quick glance at Rat's face. Rat said nothing. Anansi said nothing. They both looked at the plantains.

Then at last Anansi spoke. "My friend," he said, "what a lovely bunch of plantains! Where did you get it in these hard times?"

"It's all that I had left in my field, Anansi. This bunch must last until the peas are ready, and they are not ready yet."

"But they will be ready soon," said Anansi, "they will be ready soon. Brother Rat, give me one or two of the plantains. The children have eaten nothing, and they have only water for supper."

"All right, Anansi," said Rat. "Just wait a minute."

Rat counted all the plantains carefully and then said, "Well, perhaps, Br'er Anansi, perhaps!" Then he counted them again and finally broke off the four smallest plantains and gave them to Anansi.

"Thank you," said Anansi, "thank you, my good friend. But, Rat, it's four plantains, and there are five of us in the family—my wife, the three children, and myself."

Rat took no notice of this. He only said, "Help me to put this bunch of plantains on my head, Br'er Anansi, and do not try to break off any more."

So Anansi had to help Rat to put the bunch of plantains back on his head. Rat went off, walking slowly because of the weight of the bunch. Then Anansi set off for his home. He could walk quickly because the four plantains were not a heavy burden. When he got to his home he handed the four plantains to Crooky, his wife, and told her to roast them. He went outside and sat down in the shade of the mango tree until Crooky called out to say that the plantains were ready.

Anansi went back inside. There were the four plantains, nicely roasted. He took up one and gave it to the girl. He gave one each to the two boys. He gave the last and biggest plantain to his wife. After that he sat down empty-handed and very very sad-looking, and his wife said to him, "Don't you want some of the plantains?"

"No," said Anansi, with a deep sigh. "There are only enough for four of us. I'm hungry, too, because I haven't had anything to eat; but there are just enough for you."

The little child asked, "Aren't you hungry, Papa?"

"Yes, my child, I am hungry, but you are too little. You cannot find food for yourselves. It's better for me to remain hungry as long as your stomachs are filled."

"No, Papa," shouted the children, "you must have half of my plantain." They all broke their plantains in two, and each one gave Anansi a half. When Crooky saw what was happening she gave Anansi half of her plantain, too. So, in the end, Anansi got more than anyone, just as usual.

There are other wonderful Anansi stories in *Anansi the Spider Man* by Philip M. Sherlock, the book from which this tale came. And you might try *Ears and Tails and Common Sense: More Stories from the Caribbean* by Philip M. Sherlock and Hilary Sherlock. Or, for the West African versions, try *Ananse the Spider: Tales from an Ashanti Village* and *Tales of an Ashanti Father*, both by Peggy Appiah.

Baba Yaga's Geese

from *Baba Yaga's Geese and Other Russian Stories*
translated and adapted by Bonnie Carey

Baba Yaga is an evil witch in Russian folklore. She
flies around in a mortar steered by a pestle, and uses
a broom to wipe away all traces of her flight. She
lives in a hut that is supported on chicken legs and
spins around in all directions. As in this story, Baba
Yaga likes to steal young children.

There once lived an old lady and an old man who had a
granddaughter and a little grandson. One day they
decided to go to town.

They said to their granddaughter, "We are going to
town, Marya. We'll bring back a sweet roll and a new
kerchief for you, but you must be a good girl and take
care of your little brother. Don't go out of the yard."

The old people set out. Marya carried her brother
outside and set him down on the grass beneath the

window. Then she ran off to play in the road. Suddenly some geese flew by, snatched up the little boy, and carried him away on their backs.

Marya ran back and saw that her brother was gone. She looked all around, but he was nowhere to be seen. She called and called, but he didn't answer. She ran to an open field. There she caught a glimpse of a flock of geese disappearing in the distance. They flew over the dark forest, and then she couldn't see them anymore.

"The geese have taken away my brother," the little girl thought, and she set out after them.

She ran and ran until she saw an oven standing in her way.

"Oven, oven, tell me where the geese have flown," she said.

"Eat my pie made of rye flour and I will tell you."

Marya answered, "Why, my family and I don't even eat pies made of wheat flour!"

She ran on. She ran further and further until she came to an apple tree.

"Apple tree, apple tree, where have the geese flown?" she asked.

"Eat one of my wild apples and I will tell you."

"Why, my family and I don't even eat cultivated apples!" Marya said, hurrying on.

She ran and ran until she saw a river of milk with a pudding shore.

She said, "River of milk with your pudding shore, where have the geese flown?"

"Eat my plain milk pudding and I will tell you."

"Why, my family and I don't even eat cream pudding!" she answered and ran on.

Marya rushed on and on until she came upon a hedgehog. She wanted to push the hedgehog out of her way, but she was afraid he would prick her.

She asked, "Hedgehog, hedgehog, where have the geese flown?"

The hedgehog pointed out a path to the girl. She ran down the path and came to a clearing where she saw a hut on hen's legs twirling in every direction. Inside the hut was Baba Yaga, the Russian witch, with her bony legs and her ugly face that looks like grey clay. Marya's brother was sitting on a bench near the window, playing with a golden apple. Marya crept up to the window, grabbed her brother, and started to run home, carrying him piggyback.

Baba Yaga was watching. She quickly called her geese and sent them after the girl. Meanwhile, Baba Yaga jumped into her mortar, an enormous bowl in

which she travels around the countryside. Then she, too, flew into the air after Marya.

Marya ran fast, but Baba Yaga and the geese were overtaking her. Where could she go? She ran to the river of milk with its pudding shore.

"Dear river, please hide us!" she begged.

"Eat my plain milk pudding. Then I will hide you."

Marya had no choice. She gulped down the milk pudding. The river hid her and her brother under a steep bank, and the geese flew past. She came out from under the bank and ran further, still carrying her brother piggyback. The geese caught sight of them and chased them again. What could she do?

She ran up to the apple tree. "Dear apple tree, please hide us!"

"Eat one of my wild apples. Then I will hide you."

Marya could do nothing else. She ate one of the wild apples. The apple tree covered them with its branches, and the geese flew by with Baba Yaga close behind.

Marya came out from under the apple tree and started running home. She ran as fast as she could, but the geese caught sight of her and her brother again and began to chase them. They had almost caught up with them and were flapping their wings just above Marya's head when she reached the oven.

"Dear oven, please hide us!"

"Eat my pie made of rye flour. Then I will hide you."

The little girl quickly ate the pie made of rye flour and crawled into the oven with her brother. The geese and Baba Yaga flew by.

Then she crawled out of the oven and hurried home at full speed with her brother still on her back.

The geese caught sight of them again and went after them. They flew down and beat their wings in her face. The shadow of Baba Yaga's mortar loomed overhead. The geese were pulling Marya's brother from her hands, but the cottage was not far away. She ran into it quickly, slammed the door shut, and closed the windows. The geese circled the cottage, honking all the while. Finally, with a very angry Baba Yaga, they flew back to the hut on hen's legs and were never seen again.

The old lady and the old man came home and saw their little grandson in the house, alive and well. Marya got a sweet roll and a kerchief as her reward.

There are many other Russian folk tales in the book from which this story was taken. Another very good collection is *The Lazies: Tales of the People of Russia*, translated by Mirra Ginsburg.

The Hummingbird
by Jack Prelutsky

The ruby-throated hummingbird
is hardly bigger than this WORD.

The Hound
by Kaye Starbird

It's funny to look at a hurrying hound
Pursuing a scent that's attractive.
He gallops around
With his nose to the ground
And only the back of him active.

The Lizard
by John Gardner

The Lizard is a timid thing
That cannot dance or fly or sing;
He hunts for bugs beneath the floor
And longs to be a dinosaur.

The Frog
author unknown

What a wonderful bird the frog are—
When he stand he sit almost;
When he hop, he fly almost.
He ain't got no sense hardly;
He ain't got no tail hardly either.
When he sit, he sit on what he ain't got almost.

Clever Manka

from *The Shoemaker's Apron*
by Parker Fillmore

In many folk tales and fairy tales, people need magic
and good luck to overcome their troubles and make
wishes come true. But in this story, which comes from
Czechoslovakia, Manka doesn't need luck or magic. She
simply uses her head!

⚜ ⚜ ⚜

There was once a rich farmer who was as grasping and
unscrupulous as he was rich. He was always driving a
hard bargain and always getting the better of his poor
neighbors. One of these neighbors was a humble
shepherd who in return for service was to receive from
the farmer a heifer. When the time of payment came
the farmer refused to give the shepherd the heifer and
the shepherd was forced to lay the matter before the
burgomaster.

The burgomaster, who was a young man and as yet
not very experienced, listened to both sides and when
he had deliberated he said, "Instead of deciding this
case, I will put a riddle to you both and the man who
makes the best answer shall have the heifer. Are you
agreed?"

The farmer and the shepherd accepted this proposal
and the burgomaster said, "Well then, here is my
riddle: What is the swiftest thing in the world? What
is the sweetest thing? What is the richest? Think out
your answers and bring them to me at this same hour
tomorrow."

The farmer went home in a temper. "What kind of a
burgomaster is this young fellow!" he growled. "If he
had let me keep the heifer I'd have sent him a bushel
of pears. But now I'm in a fair way of losing the heifer
for I can't think of any answer to his foolish riddle."

"What is the matter, husband?" his wife asked.

"It's that new burgomaster. The old one would have given me the heifer without any argument, but this young man thinks to decide the case by asking us riddles."

When he told his wife what the riddle was, she cheered him greatly by telling him that she knew the answers at once.

"Why, husband," said she, "our gray mare must be the swiftest thing in the world. You know yourself nothing ever passes us on the road. As for the sweetest, did you ever taste honey any sweeter than ours? And I'm sure there's nothing richer than our chest of golden ducats that we've been laying by these forty years."

The farmer was delighted. "You're right, wife, you're right! That heifer remains ours!"

The shepherd when he got home was downcast and sad. He had a daughter, a clever girl named Manka, who met him at the door of his cottage and asked, "What is it, father? What did the burgomaster say?"

The shepherd sighed. "I'm afraid I've lost the heifer. The burgomaster set us a riddle and I know I shall never guess it."

"Perhaps I can help you," Manka said. "What is it?"

So the shepherd gave her the riddle and the next day as he was setting out for the burgomaster's, Manka told him what answers to make.

When he reached the burgomaster's house, the farmer was already there rubbing his hands and beaming with self-importance.

The burgomaster again propounded the riddle and then asked the farmer his answers.

The farmer cleared his throat and with a pompous air began, "The swiftest thing in the world? Why, my dear sir, that's my gray mare, of course, for no other horse ever passes us on the road. The sweetest? Honey from my beehives, to be sure. The richest? What can be richer than my chest of golden ducats!"

And the farmer squared his shoulders and smiled triumphantly.

"H'm," said the young burgomaster, dryly. Then he asked, "What answers does the shepherd make?"

The shepherd bowed politely and said, "The swiftest thing in the world is thought for thought can run any distance in the twinkling of an eye. The sweetest thing of all is sleep for when a man is tired and sad what can be sweeter? The richest thing is the earth for out of the earth come all the riches of the world."

"Good!" the burgomaster cried. "Good! The heifer goes to the shepherd!"

Later the burgomaster said to the shepherd, "Tell me, now, who gave you those answers? I'm sure they never came out of your own head."

At first the shepherd tried not to tell, but when the burgomaster pressed him he confessed that they came from his daughter, Manka. The burgomaster, who thought that he would like to make another test of Manka's cleverness, sent for ten eggs. He gave them to the shepherd and said, "Take these eggs to Manka and tell her to have them hatched out by tomorrow and to bring me the chicks."

When the shepherd reached home and gave Manka the burgomaster's message, Manka laughed and said: "Take a handful of millet and go right back to the burgomaster. Say to him: 'My daughter sends you this millet. She says that if you plant, grow it, and have it harvested by tomorrow, she'll bring you the ten chicks and you can feed them the ripe grain.'"

When the burgomaster heard this, he laughed heartily.

"That's a clever girl of yours," he told the shepherd. "If she's as comely as she is clever, I think I'd like to marry her. Tell her to come to see me, but she must come neither by day nor by night, neither riding nor walking, neither dressed nor undressed."

When Manka received this message she waited until the next dawn when night was gone and day not yet arrived. Then she wrapped herself in a fishnet and, throwing one leg over a goat's back and keeping one foot on the ground, she went to the burgomaster's house.

Now I ask you: did she go dressed? No, she wasn't dressed. A fishnet isn't clothing. Did she go undressed? Of course not, for wasn't she covered with a fishnet? Did she walk to the burgomaster's? No, she didn't walk for she went with one leg thrown over a goat. Then did she ride? Of course she didn't ride for wasn't she walking on one foot?

When she reached the burgomaster's house she called out, "Here I am, Mr. Burgomaster, and I've come

neither by day nor by night, neither riding nor walking, neither dressed nor undressed."

The young burgomaster was so delighted with Manka's cleverness and so pleased with her comely looks that he proposed to her at once and in a short time married her.

"But understand, my dear Manka," he said, "you are not to use that cleverness of yours at my expense. I won't have you interfering in any of my cases. In fact if ever you give advice to any one who comes to me for judgment, I'll turn you out of my house at once and send you home to your father."

All went well for a time. Manka busied herself in her house-keeping and was careful not to interfere in any of the burgomaster's cases.

Then one day two farmers came to the burgomaster to have a dispute settled. One of the farmers owned a mare which had foaled in the marketplace. The colt had run under the wagon of the other farmer and thereupon the owner of the wagon claimed the colt as his property.

The burgomaster, who was thinking of something else while the case was being presented, said carelessly, "The man who found the colt under his wagon is, of course, the owner of the colt."

As the owner of the mare was leaving the burgomaster's house, he met Manka and stopped to tell her about the case. Manka was ashamed of her husband for making so foolish a decision and she said to the farmer, "Come back this afternoon with a fishing net and stretch it across the dusty road. When the burgomaster sees you he will come out and ask you what you are doing. Say to him that you're catching fish. When he asks you how you can expect to catch fish in a dusty road, tell him it's just as easy for you to catch fish in a dusty road as it is for a wagon to foal. Then he'll see the injustice of his decision and have the colt returned to you. But remember one thing: you mustn't let him find out that it was I who told you to do this."

That afternoon when the burgomaster chanced to look out the window he saw a man stretching a fishnet across the dusty road. He went out to him and asked, "What are you doing?"

"Fishing."

"Fishing in a dusty road? Are you daft?"

"Well," the man said, "it's just as easy for me to catch fish in a dusty road as it is for a wagon to foal."

Then the burgomaster recognized the man as the owner of the mare and he had to confess that what he said was true. "Of course the colt belongs to your mare and must be returned to you. But tell me," he said, "who put you up to this? You didn't think of it yourself."

The farmer tried not to tell but the burgomaster questioned him until he found out that Manka was at the bottom of it. This made him very angry. He went into the house and called his wife.

"Manka," he said, "do you forget what I told you would happen if you went interfering in any of my cases? Home you go this very day. I don't care to hear any excuses. The matter is settled. You may take with you the one thing you like best in my house for I won't have people saying that I treated you shabbily."

Manka made no outcry. "Very well, my dear husband, I shall do as you say: I shall go to my father's cottage and take with me the one thing I like best in your house. But don't make me go until after supper. We have been very happy together and I should like to eat one last meal with you. Let us have no more words but be kind to each other as we've always been and then part as friends."

The burgomaster agreed to this and Manka prepared a fine supper of all the dishes of which her husband was particularly fond. The burgomaster opened his choicest wine and pledged Manka's health. Then he set to, and the supper was so good that he ate and ate and ate. And the more he ate, the more he drank until at last he grew drowsy and fell sound asleep in his chair. Then without awakening him Manka had him carried out to the wagon that was waiting to take her home to her father.

The next morning when the burgomaster opened his eyes, he found himself lying in the shepherd's cottage.

"What does this mean?" he roared out.

"Nothing, dear husband, nothing!" Manka said. "You know you told me I might take with me the one thing I liked best in your house, so of course I took you! That's all."

For a moment the burgomaster rubbed his eyes in amazement. Then he laughed loud and heartily to think how Manka had outwitted him.

"Manka," he said, "you're too clever for me. Come on, my dear, let's go home."

So they climbed back into the wagon and drove home.

The burgomaster never again scolded his wife but thereafter whenever a very difficult case came up he always said, "I think we had better consult my wife. You know she's a very clever woman."

There are all kinds of ways to make fairy-tale wishes come true. In *Clever Gretchen and Other Forgotten Stories*, retold by Alison Lurie, you'll find fifteen stories about girls who trick giants, answer riddles, rescue friends, and have other exciting adventures. In some folk tales animals use their heads as well as people do. Read *The Lion Sneezed* by Maria Leech to meet a collection of clever cats who outwit their enemies.

Casey at the Bat

by Ernest Lawrence Thayer

The outlook wasn't brilliant for the Mudville nine that day;
The score stood four to two, with but one inning more to play;
And so, when Cooney died at first, and Barrows did the same,
A sickly silence fell upon the patrons of the game.

A straggling few got up to go in deep despair. The rest
Clung to the hope which springs eternal in the human breast;
They thought, if only Casey could but get a whack, at that,
They'd put up even money now, with Casey at the bat.

But Flynn preceded Casey, as did also Jimmy Blake,
And the former was a pudding and the latter was a fake;
So upon that striken multitude grim melancholy sat,
For there seemed but little chance of Casey's getting to the bat.

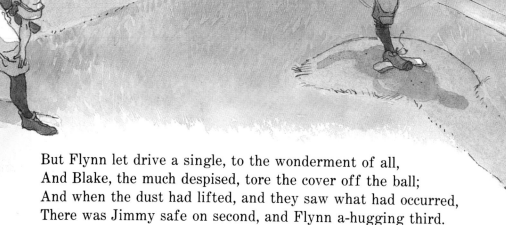

But Flynn let drive a single, to the wonderment of all,
And Blake, the much despised, tore the cover off the ball;
And when the dust had lifted, and they saw what had occurred,
There was Jimmy safe on second, and Flynn a-hugging third.

Then from the gladdened multitude went up a joyous yell,
It bounded from the mountain-top, and rattled in the dell;
It struck upon the hillside, and recoiled upon the flat;
For Casey, mighty Casey, was advancing to the bat.

There was ease in Casey's manner as he stepped into his place,
There was pride in Casey's bearing, and a smile on Casey's face;
And when, responding to the cheers, he lightly doffed his hat,
No stranger in the crowd could doubt 'twas Casey at the bat.

Ten thousand eyes were on him as he rubbed his hands with dirt,
Five thousand tongues applauded when he wiped them on his shirt;
Then while the writhing pitcher ground the ball into his hip,
Defiance gleamed in Casey's eye, a sneer curled Casey's lip.

And now the leather-covered sphere came hurtling through the air,
And Casey stood a-watching it in haughty grandeur there;
Close by the sturdy batsman the ball unheeded sped.
"That ain't my style," said Casey. "Strike one," the umpire said.

From the benches, black with people, there went a muffled roar,
Like the beating of the storm-waves on a stern and distant shore;
"Kill him! kill the umpire!" shouted someone on the stand.
And it's likely they'd have killed him had not Casey raised his hand.

With a smile of Christian charity great Casey's visage shone;
He stilled the rising tumult; he bade the game go on;
He signalled to the pitcher, and once more the spheroid flew,
But Casey still ignored it, and the umpire said, "Strike two."

"Fraud!" cried the maddened thousands, and the echo answered, "Fraud!"
But a scornful look from Casey, and the audience was awed;
They saw his face grow stern and cold, they saw his muscles strain,
And they knew that Casey wouldn't let that ball go by again.

The sneer is gone from Casey's lips, his teeth are clenched in hate,
He pounds with cruel violence his bat upon the plate;
And now the pitcher holds the ball, and now he lets it go,
And now the air is shattered by the force of Casey's blow.

Oh! somewhere in this favored land the sun is shining bright,
The band is playing somewhere, and somewhere hearts are light;
And somewhere men are laughing, and somewhere children shout,
But there is no joy in Mudville—mighty Casey has struck out.

Nina Terrance

from *The Cry of the Crow*
by Jean Craighead George

Mandy Tressel awakes to the sound of gun blasts. Her
father or older brothers, Jack and Carver, must be
hunting crows in Piney Woods. Even Drummer, her
younger brother, can hardly wait until he is old
enough to hunt. Later that day, Mandy finds an
orphaned baby crow and names her Nina Terrance.
Determined to care for Nina, she makes a hidden nest
on the ground. Somehow, Mandy must keep her father
and brothers from finding her new pet.

⚜ ⚜ ⚜

Later that afternoon Kray, the leader of the Trumpet
Hammock crows, flew over Piney Woods and, spotting
black feathers on the ground, focused acutely on them
by rounding the curvature of his eye lens as crows do.

He dropped down on a tree limb near the skirted
sable palm and stared. Unlike people, who have one
central point of sharp vision, birds have two—one in
the center of the retina and one in the rear. These,

together with his overall crow vision, gave Kray three
simultaneous views of the feathers, from each side and
forward. What he saw said: "murdered crow."

"Nevah, nevah," he mourned. His cry traveled
through the forest, rolled out over the saw grass, and
penetrated the dark niches and hollows of Trumpet
Hammock.

At the sound every crow froze where it was. It was
as if none existed. Extensions on stubs appeared,
however, black knots on limbs, but no crows. They had
become one with the inanimate things of the forest.

Nina Terrance heard Kray's doomsday
pronouncement and looked at him through a hole in the
leaves. Her stomach pinched with hunger; her legs
wobbled from lack of nourishment. She needed only to
cry the begging note of the eyas crow and Kray, or
any other nearby crow, would drop down and feed the
orphan, but she was rendered silent by his "sad crow"
cry.

Still eyeing the black feathers, Kray sidled along the
limb, then walked up a bough like a shadow. When he
reached the top of the tree he spread his wings. A
wind gusted under them, lifted him, and carried him
sideways toward the hammock.

"Nevah, nevah," he moaned once more, then called sharply, "Caia," for crows call "caw" when they are flying away from their roost, "caia" when they are coming home.

An hour of silence passed, then the birds began to move again.

Nina Terrance turned her head. A beetle crept along the fingerlike edges of one of the palm leaves that made her nest. She watched it, but she was still unable to coordinate beak and eye to catch it. She had, however, today fanned her wings for the first time. Yesterday she had run her beak across her back feathers. Each day she could do one more bird skill as she developed toward being a bird that could fly.

When at sunset Kray announced the end of the day with one clear "Caw," the eyas shook herself and nestled down in her Mandy-made nest. Her hunger was unbearable. She closed her eyes and slowed down her breathing to conserve energy.

Promptly at sunup, when she could see, she flopped to the edge of the nest and prepared to fling herself to the ground and cry until the crows of Trumpet Hammock came and fed her.

Crunch da dum. She could not move. The sound of the hunter's footsteps immobilized her. *Crunch da dum, crunch da dum.* Far away now, *crunch da dum.*

The sun touched the top of the pines and Kray announced the start of the day. His clan awoke and yawned, then silently preened their feathers to make them airtight for flight. The eyases in well-hidden nests opened their eyes. One was old enough to shake himself, three days more advanced than Nina Terrance.

Presently an adult crow designated himself guard crow for the morning, for the crows rotate this duty. He sailed to a stub on an old cypress tree, where he scanned the river of grass, the distant highway, Waterway Village, and the strawberry field. The berries matured later than most of Florida's strawberry crop, for they were a unique cross between a wild strawberry of the north and the enormous cultivated berries of Florida and California. Their flavor was piquant and sugar sweet, and they were very much in demand in fancy restaurants. The guard crow did not even glance at them. The "sad crow" call of yesterday had linked death to the woods.

The door of the cinder-block house opened and Mandy came out. The guard crow knew her as he did her mother. He considered them both harmless "large rabbits" of the yard and paths and was unafraid of them.

"Caaa caa ca," he called to the clan—a signal that meant disperse and go hunt. One by one the crows flapped through the trees and coasted on partially extended wings out across the Glades, then beat their way toward the distant highway where they scouted for road kill. The guard bird watched them go, flattening his eye lens to keep them in focus three and four miles away. Then he glanced out of the back of his eyes and scanned for enemies: snakes, rats, owls, hawks, anything that might threaten the precious eyases.

When the crows were gone, the mockingbirds and wrens flew to their singing posts and announced ownership of their part of the forest edge.

Nina Terrance was listening to them when she felt Mandy push back the huge leaves and enter the sable palm tent.

"Hi, Nina Terrance," she said. "I can't stay long. I sneaked out of the house before Daddy got up, to feed you and to make sure you're all right." Cupping her hands, she lifted Nina out of her nest and placed her on the ground. Dipping a piece of cheese sandwich in a jar of milk, she held it out for Nina Terrance. The bird instantly recognized the offering as food although she had never seen bread and cheese before. She fluttered her wings and begged. Mandy stuffed her mouth and broke off another bite.

As Nina Terrance ate she changed the shape of her eye lenses from flat to round and back again. Then she blinked. Something was happening to her mind. Mandy was becoming her mother and she, Nina Terrance, was becoming Mandy. Her feathers in her bird mind were knitting into human clothing, her head was becoming covered with brown hair, and her wings were feeling like hands.

Mandy was being imprinted on her mind, because whoever feeds a baby bird is stamped upon its brain as

a parent, be it a mechanical toy bird or a little girl. The bird thereafter considers itself to be like the toy or the human.

By the end of the feeding Nina Terrance was looking with adoration at her mother, whom she now thought she resembled. Her mother picked her up, held her close, and after smelling her sweet feathers put her in the nest.

"Stay still until I come back," she said.

"Ay," croaked Nina Terrance, fluttering her throat to effect an imitation of her mother's voice.

When Mandy reached home her father was at his desk in the living room making notes in his account book. He struggled, head down, shoulders rounded over the work, for Fred Tressel had never completed sixth grade and arithmetic came hard to him. He was only comfortable when he was out in the greenhouse or field crossbreeding his famous stock of strawberries and, when a good strain came along, an occasional tomato or pepper. Mandy's mother, Barbara, often said Fred Tressel was related to the pollinating bee.

Mandy paused on a dark step to watch this huge man who had grown up planting vegetables and

fruits—and also hunting alligators until they were protected by the National Park. When he smiled, which was most of the time, he did not seem like a person who could shoot crows. Once Mandy had asked him why he did it, and he had answered: "My family comes first. Our crops are our living."

This had not been a very satisfactory answer for Mandy because, one, she had never seen a crow in the strawberry patch, and two, crows were small and helpless like Nina Terrance.

She must ask him again, she thought as she crawled back into bed with her clothes on and waited until she heard her father fixing his breakfast in the kitchen below.

The clank of pans was her usual signal to get up. She arose, brushed her hair, and listened as she did every morning to Jack and Carver shouting in the shower and banging doors. In the cacophony of morning in the Tressel home she ran down the stairs and hurried through the living room and across the hall to her parents' room.

Her mother was seated at her dressing table brushing her short brown hair and coaxing the front curls into waves.

"Hi, honey," she said upon seeing Mandy in the mirror. "You look like you've swallowed an alligator. What's up?"

The door banged as her father went out to the strawberry field. Mandy sat down on the bed and patted the green slacks and shirt her mother had laid out for herself. She worked weekdays at the Agricultural Experiment Station at the north end of town.

"I have a new friend," she said.

"That's wonderful. What's her name?" Her mother peered closer at herself and rubbed a freckle on her cheek.

"Nina Terrance."

"That's an interesting name. Is she Puerto Rican?"

"No."

"Too bad, I hoped maybe she could help me. Maria and Teresa will be helping with the strawberry crop again and I can't always understand them."

"You speak good Spanish, Mommy," said Mandy, smoothing the collar of the shirt on the bed.

"Well, I'm learning, but I could use help. And I hoped your new friend . . ."

"Nina Terrance can't possibly help," Mandy said so forcibly that Barbara looked again at her daughter's reflection in the mirror.

"I just wondered if she could, that's all. What color is your friend's hair?"

"Black."

"And her eyes?"

"A pale milky blue."

"Pale milky blue? Good heavens, Mandy, she sounds odd." Barbara Tressel slowly swung around on her stool and peered at her daughter. "What do her parents do?" she asked suspiciously.

"Fly."

"They do? Where does she live?"

"In Piney Woods."

"Oh, Mandy. Are you sure you should keep this friend?" Mandy slid off the bed and walked to her mother's side.

"Yes, Mommy. I am."

"You know how your dad feels about crows?" She looked directly into Mandy's eyes. "I mean how he *really* feels about them."

"Yes."

"And you think you should go ahead with this?"

"I'll keep her out of his sight in the woods."

Barbara slowly brushed her hair.

"Where are her parents?"

"Dead. All the crows of Piney Woods are dead. Daddy and Jack and Carver shot them all—all but Nina Terrance."

Barbara winced.

"I think you ought to talk to your father about this. He might not be as terrible as you think."

"But he is. He shoots crows."

"He also knows a lot about crows and might be able to help you. He says crows are vindictive and remember forever the persons who shoot at them. You wouldn't want that crow hurting Daddy or Jack or Carver, would you?"

Mandy did not answer.

"Maybe your dad knows how to erase an imprint of a killer in a crow's mind. Then it wouldn't hurt anyone."

"How could a crow possibly hurt anyone? Nina Terrance is small and gentle."

Barbara shrugged and changed the subject.

"Have you written any more stories?"

Mandy was about to say no, then changed her mind.

"One. For *The Waterway Times*."

"Good. Are they going to run it?"

"No."

"Shoot," said Barbara with feeling. "Older brothers sure can be difficult. I had three."

Mandy's head drooped, and she took her mother's hand.

"Why won't they let me be part of the newspaper? Drummer is and he's just a little boy."

"I don't know, Mandy. I really don't know." She ran her fingers through Mandy's hair. "But I think it is something about practicing being dominant so they can compete out in the world. Soon Jack and Carver will have to seek their fortunes, so to speak."

"I do want to be a reporter for them. They have such a good time working together on that paper."

"Never mind, Mandy. You're wonderful."

"I'm not. I'm lonely. Loners don't grow and learn. I'll stay dumb." She slipped her arm around her mother and buried her face in her breast. Barbara hugged her.

"But you have a remarkable friend now in Nina Terrance."

Mandy blinked back her tears and smiled up at her mother.

"Nina Terrance attends a private school," said Mandy.

"Wow, she must be rich."

"Very rich. She has a favorite charity."

"She does?" Barbara knitted her brow trying to figure out where the game was leading.

"Yes, a poor family on the other side of Piney Woods."

"Oh, I see," Barbara nodded. "We must pack food boxes for them."

"Exactly," said Mandy, clapping her hands in the excitement of their fantasy world. "And she can't visit me. Her parents are very protective."

"Of course," Barbara squeezed Mandy's hand. "I would never have thought of that."

"I met her in the dentist's office. She has braces too."

"That's getting pretty complicated. Do you have to have met her in the dentist's office?"

"I've already told Drummer I did."

"Well, we had better stick with that. What else did you tell him about her?"

"That's all." Mandy threw herself back on the bed again. "Except that she's rich and has a charity."

"Good." Barbara became silent as if weighing the wisdom of Mandy's keeping the crow.

"How can I tell which is the alarm cry?" Mandy had sensed her change of heart and was trying to get her more involved. It worked.

"Watch old Kray, the boss bird that Drummer named," Barbara said. "I don't know which one he is, but your daddy says when he or Jack or Carver come near Trumpet Hammock, he gives the alarm cry and all his clan vanishes from sight."

"Does he give it when we come out?"

"No. He knows they hunt and kill crows and we don't." Barbara was smiling helplessly at her daughter. "Mandy, I'm such a sucker for this. Shall we pack a nice charity box for Nina Terrance's poor family?"

"You're going to play," Mandy exclaimed happily. "Oh, Mommy, you're going to love Nina Terrance."

"Yes, I'm afraid I am. Crows are fascinating, but you'll have to keep this one away from the farm."

"I can do it."

"Well, baby crows like to follow the parent that feeds them. You'll have to be clever. Doctor Bert, at the Experiment Station, is an expert on crows, too. I'll ask him what to do today and bring you some of the bulletins he writes about their behavior and food habits. Crows are social birds—that is, they live and work together like we people do. They are very intelligent, too. Your dad says they can even count. If three hunters go into a woods where a roost is, and two of them leave, the crows won't appear until the third hunter departs."

"Daddy would want me to play with an intelligent friend, wouldn't he?"

Barbara laughed and buttoned her shirt. "He certainly would."

Mandy soon learns how clever her pet is—and how much trouble, too. Read *The Cry of the Crow* to find out more about Nina Terrance and the problems she creates. The author, Jean Craighead George, has written many books about nature and wildlife, such as *My Side of the Mountain* and *Julie of the Wolves*, which won the Newbery Medal.

142

Glooscap and His People

from *Glooscap and His Magic: Legends of
the Wabanaki Indians* by Kay Hill

Glooscap is the great culture hero of the Wabanaki (or
Abnaki) Indians of Eastern Canada and the
northeastern United States. Here is one of many
legends about this super being.

⚜ ⚜ ⚜

In the Old Time, long before the White Man came, the
Indians believed that every rock and river, every tree
and bird and animal, possessed a spirit—and some
spirits were good and some were evil. Around these
spirits, which they pictured as giants and wizards and
magical animals, the Indians invented marvelous
stories called "atookwakuns," or wonder tales. They tell
these stories to amuse the children, even to this day,
and the stories the children love best are the stories of
Glooscap and his People.

In the beginning, the Indians tell the children, there
was just the forest and the sea—no people and no
animals. Then Glooscap came. Where this wondrous
giant was born and when, they cannot tell, but he
came from somewhere in the Sky with Malsum his
twin brother to the part of North America nearest the
rising sun. There, anchoring his canoe, he turned it
into a granite island covered with spruce and pine. He
called the island Uktamkoo, the land we know today as
Newfoundland. This, in the beginning, was Glooscap's
lodge.

The Great Chief looked and lived like an ordinary
Indian except that he was twice as tall and twice as
strong, and possessed great magic. He was never sick,
never married, never grew old, and never died. He had
a magic belt which gave him great power, and he used
this power only for good. Malsum, his brother, also

great of stature, had the head of a wolf and the body of an Indian. He knew magic too, but he used his power for evil.

It was the warm time when Glooscap came. As he set about his work, the air was fragrant with balsam and the tang of the sea. First, out of the rocks, he made the Little People—the fairies, or Megumoowesoos, small hairy creatures who dwelt among the rocks and made wonderful music on the flute, such music that all who heard it were bewitched. From amongst them, Glooscap chose a servant, Marten, who was like a younger brother to him.

Next Glooscap made men. Taking up his great bow, he shot arrows into the trunks of ash trees. Out of the trees stepped men and women. They were a strong and graceful people with light brown skins and shining black hair, and Glooscap called them the Wabanaki, which means "those who live where the day breaks." In time, the Wabanaki left Uktamkoo and divided into separate tribes and are today a part of the great Algonquin nation—but in the old days only the Micmacs, Malicetes, Penobscots and Passamaquoddies, living in the eastern woodlands of Canada and the United States, were Glooscap's People.

Gazing upon his handiwork, Glooscap was pleased and his shout of triumph made the tall pines bend like grass.

He told the people he was their Great Chief and would rule them with love and justice. He taught them how to build birchbark wigwams and canoes, how to make weirs for catching fish, and how to identify plants useful in medicine. He taught them the names of all the Stars, who were his brothers.

Then, from among them, he chose an elderly woman whom he called Noogumee, or grandmother, which is a term of respect amongst Indians for any elderly female. Noogumee was the Great Chief's housekeeper all her days.

Now, finally, out of rocks and clay, Glooscap made
the animals—Miko the Squirrel, Team the Moose,
Mooin the Bear, and many, many others. Malsum
looked on enviously, thinking he too should have had a
hand in creation, but he had not been given that
power. However, he whispered an evil charm, and the
remainder of the clay in Glooscap's hands twisted and
fell to the ground in the form of a strange animal—not
beaver, not badger, not wolverine, but something of all

three, and capable of taking any of these forms he chose.

"His name is Lox!" said Malsum triumphantly.

"So be it," said Glooscap. "Let Lox live amongst us in peace, so long as he remains a friend." Yet he resolved to watch Lox closely, for he could read the heart and knew that Lox had Malsum's evil in him.

Now Glooscap had made the animals all very large, most of them larger and stronger than man. Lox, the troublemaker, at once saw his chance to make mischief.

He went in his wolverine body to Team the Moose and admired his fine antlers, which reached up to the top of the tallest pine tree. "If you should ever meet a man," said Lox, "you could toss him on your horns up to the top of the world."

Now Team, who was just a little bit stupid, went at once to Glooscap and said, "Please, Master, give me a man, so I can toss him on my horns up to the top of the world!"

"I should say not!" cried Glooscap, touching Team with his hand—and the moose was suddenly the size he is today.

Then Lox went in his badger form to the squirrel and said, "With that magnificent tail of yours, Miko, you could smash down every lodge in the village."

"So I could," said Miko proudly, and with his great tail he swept the nearest wigwam right off the ground. But the Great Chief was near. He caught Miko up in his hand and stroked the squirrel's back until he was as small as he is today.

"From now on," said his Master, "you will live in trees and keep your tail where it belongs." And since that time Miko the Squirrel has carried his bushy tail on his·back.

Next, the rascally Lox put on his beaver shape and went to Mooin the Bear, who was hardly any bigger than he is today, but had a much larger throat.

"Mooin," said Lox slyly, "supposing you met a man, what would you do to him?" The bear scratched his head thoughtfully. "Eat him," he said at last, with a grin. "Yes, that's what I'd do—I'd swallow him whole!" And having said this, Mooin felt his throat begin to shrink.

"From now on," said Glooscap sternly, "you may swallow only very small creatures." And today the bear, big as he is, eats only small animals, fish and wild berries.

Now the Great Chief was greatly annoyed at the way his animals were behaving, and wondered if he ought to have made them. He summoned them all and gave them a solemn warning:

"I have made you man's equal, but you wish to be his master. Take care—or he may become yours!"

This did not worry the troublemaker Lox, who only resolved to be more cunning in the future. He knew very well that Malsum was jealous of Glooscap and wished to be lord of the Indians himself. He also knew that both brothers had magic powers and that neither could be killed except in one certain way. What that way was, each kept secret—from all but the Stars, whom they trusted. Each sometimes talked in the starlight to the people of the Sky.

"Little does Malsum know," said Glooscap to the Stars, "that I can never be killed except by the blow of a flowering rush." And not far off, Malsum boasted to those same Stars—"I am quite safe from Glooscap's power. I can do anything I like, for nothing can harm me but the roots of a flowering fern."

Now, alas, Lox was hidden close by and overheard both secrets. Seeing how he might turn this to his own advantage, he went to Malsum and said with a knowing smile, "What will you give me, Malsum, if I tell you Glooscap's secret?"

"Anything you like," cried Malsum. "Quick—tell me!"

"Nothing can hurt Glooscap save a flowering rush," said the traitor. "Now give me a pair of wings, like the pigeon, so I can fly."

But Malsum laughed.

"What need has a beaver of wings?" And kicking the troublemaker aside, he sped to find a flowering rush. Lox picked himself up furiously and hurried to Glooscap.

"Master!" he cried, "Malsum knows your secret and is about to kill you. If you would save yourself, know that only a fern root can destroy him!"

Glooscap snatched up the nearest fern, root and all, just in time—for his evil brother was upon him, shouting his war cry. And all the animals, who were

angry at Glooscap for reducing their size and power,
cheered Malsum; but the Indians were afraid for their
Master.

Glooscap braced his feet against a cliff, and Malsum
paused. For a moment, the two crouched face to face,
waiting for the moment to strike. Then the wolf-like
Malsum lunged at Glooscap's head. Twisting his body
aside, the Great Chief flung his weapon. It went swift
to its target, and Malsum leapt back—too late. The
fern root pierced his envious heart, and he died.

Now the Indians rejoiced, and the animals crept
sullenly away. Only Lox came to Glooscap, impudently.

"I'll have my reward now, Master," he said, "a pair
of wings, like the pigeon's."

"Faithless creature!" Glooscap thundered, knowing
full well who had betrayed him, "*I* made no such
bargain. Begone!" And he hurled stone after stone at
the fleeing Lox. Where the stones fell—in Minas
Basin—they turned into islands and are there still.

And the banished Lox roams the world to this day, appealing to the evil in men's hearts and making trouble wherever he goes.

Now Glooscap called his people around him and said, "I made the animals to be man's friends, but they have acted with selfishness and treachery. Hereafter, they shall be your servants and provide you with food and clothing."

Then he showed the men how to make bows and arrows and stone-tipped spears, and how to use them. He also showed the women how to scrape hides and turn them into clothing.

"Now you have power over even the largest wild creatures," he said. "Yet I charge you to use this power gently. If you take more game than you need for food and clothing, or kill for the pleasure of killing, then you will be visited by a pitiless giant named Famine, and when he comes among men, they suffer hunger and die."

The Indians readily promised to obey Glooscap in this, as in all things. But now, to their dismay, they saw Marten launch the Master's canoe and Noogumee entering it with Glooscap's household goods. Glooscap was leaving them!

"I must dwell now in a separate place," said the Great Chief, "so that you, my people, will learn to stand alone, and become brave and resourceful. Nevertheless, I shall never be far from you, and whoever seeks me diligently in time of trouble will find me."

Then, waving farewell to his sorrowful Wabanaki, Glooscap set off for the mainland. Rounding the southern tip of what is now Nova Scotia, the Great Chief paddled up the Bay of Fundy. In the distance, where the Bay narrows and the great tides of Fundy rush into Minas Basin, Glooscap saw a long purple headland, like a moose swimming, with clouds for

antlers, and headed his canoe in that direction. Landing, he gazed at the slope of red sandstone, with its groves of green trees at the summit, and admired the amethysts encircling its base like a string of purple beads.

"Here I shall build my lodge," said Glooscap, and he named the place Blomidon.

Now Glooscap dwelt on Blomidon a very long time, and during that time did many wonderful things for his People. Of these things you will hear in the pages to follow.

But for the present, *kespeadooksit*, which means "the story ends."

Glooscap and His Magic by Kay Hill, the book from which this story was taken, contains many other fine tales about Glooscap. You may also want to read other Indian legends, such as *Skunny Wundy: Seneca Indian Tales* by Arthur C. Parker and *Tonweya and the Eagles and Other Lakota Indian Tales* by Rosebud Yellow Robe.

Do You Fear the Wind?
by Hamlin Garland

Do you fear the force of the wind,
The slash of the rain?
Go face them and fight them,
Be savage again.
Go hungry and cold like the wolf,
Go wade like the crane:
The palms of your hands will thicken,
The skin of your cheek will tan,
You'll grow ragged and weary and swarthy,
But you'll walk like a man!

Wind-Wolves
by William D. Sargent

Do you hear the cry as the pack goes by,
The wind-wolves hunting across the sky?
Hear them tongue it, keen and clear,
Hot on the flanks of the flying deer!

Across the forest, mere, and plain,
Their hunting howl goes up again!
All night they'll follow the ghostly trail,
All night we'll hear their phantom wail,

For tonight the wind-wolf pack holds sway
From Pegasus Square to the Milky Way,
And the frightened bands of cloud-deer flee
In scattered groups of two and three.

The Wolf
by Georgia Roberts Durston

When the pale moon hides and the wild wind wails,
And over the tree-tops the nighthawk sails,
The gray wolf sits on the world's far rim,
And howls: and it seems to comfort him.

The wolf is a lonely soul, you see,
No beast in the wood, nor bird in the tree,
But shuns his path; in the windy gloom
They give him plenty, and plenty of room.

So he sits with his long, lean face to the sky
Watching the ragged clouds go by.
There in the night, alone, apart,
Singing the song of his lone, wild heart.

Far away, on the world's dark rim
He howls, and it seems to comfort him.

The Wolf Cry
by Lew Sarett

The Arctic moon hangs overhead;
The wide white silence lies below.
A starveling pine stands lone and gaunt,
Black-penciled on the snow.

Weird as the moan of sobbing winds,
A lone long call floats up from the trail;
And the naked soul of the frozen North
Trembles in that wail.

A New Way

from *Toolmaker*
by Jill Paton Walsh

This story takes place many thousands of years ago,
in the time called the Stone Age, when people made
and used stone tools. Ra is a fine toolmaker, and his
skill leads to a new way of life.

⚜ ⚜ ⚜

On the grassy slopes in the shelter of the wood, and
just a little above the stream, Ra's tribe were busy
making shelters for the summer, each family building
one hut. They dug away the earth of the hillside till
they got down to a solid, firm floor; then they made a
framework of branches, and stretched over it tents
made of skins. There were many skins in a tent, all
carefully stitched together with overlapping edges to
keep out the wind and rain. Ra had not earned one
yet—his hut would be covered in bracken and
brushwood. He looked enviously at the others. Nearly
all the huts were almost finished, but only the

Great-grandmother's was completely ready, for everyone had to help with hers before starting their own. Ra's house was slowest of all because he had nobody helping him. Among the forest tribes a boy lived with his mother's and grandmother's family; but Ra's mother had died in the snows of the winter which was just passing, and he had not yet gathered enough skins and bones and flint tools to buy himself a wife, and join her family. So for the time being he was alone, and had to live in a hut by himself.

He had scraped an earth floor out of the grassy slope. Now he was making a ring of pliable sticks set upright in the ground all around it. He set to work with the new bundle. First he made a hole by driving a piece of bone into the ground with a large stone for a hammer. Then he rocked the bone drill to and fro, pulled it out of the ground, and set the hazel branch in the hole, wedging it firmly with a little loose earth. Soon the ring of sticks was finished, with a gap in it for a door. Ra unwound from his waist a long strip of leather, and reaching up he bent the hazel branches down over his head one by one, and tied them into a bundle with his thong.

It was getting dark now, and Ra went hastily down to the stream to find a piece of flint in the pebbles in the water, to make himself a new axe. There was no time now to gather bracken to cover the framework of his hut—that would have to wait till tomorrow. He found a big heavy stone of the right sort, and then went to one of the bright fires which now blazed on the slope.

He bowed to the grandmother of the family, who sat between the fire and the door-hole of the hut, in the place of honour.

"Is there room beside your fire, mother?" he asked her.

"Sit Ra, there is room," she said. Ra sat down a

little way outside the family circle, and began to make
his new axe, working in the firelight where it fell
between the shadows of Brun and Mi, a boy and girl
only a little older than Ra. First Ra broke his stone in
two against the ground. Then he chose the better half,
and wedged it firmly against his bent knee on the
ground. Then he took from his leather pouch a short
piece of the leg bone of a stag, and placing one end
against the axe stone, first here, and then there, he
struck the other end with the rejected half of the
stone, making flakes of flint fly off in all directions.

   Ra was good at making axes, but the light was poor,
and he bent closely over his work. Even so he could
feel that someone was watching him. Ra glanced up,

hoping it was Mi, and his eyes met those of Yul. Yul was a grown man, tall and strong, some said the best hunter in the tribe. And he had hunted with Ra's father long ago. Ra was in awe of him; he looked away quickly. When he had finished his axe he stood up to go.

"May the hunt be good tomorrow to those who shared fire with me tonight," he said.

In his own unfinished house he lay down to sleep. There was nothing else to do, for the day had gone in travelling, and in hut making, there had been no time to hunt, and so there was nothing to eat. Ra was used to going to bed with an empty stomach, but all winter he had slept in a deep cave in the distant hills, and he was not used to sleeping in the open. The year had only just begun to turn warmer, and the leaves were scarcely breaking bud on the trees when the Great-grandmother had moved them out of the caves. It was still sharply cold, and a wind swept the sloping glade. Shivering, Ra wished he had finished his house. Through the web of sticks over his head he could see the cold stars—the distant camp fires of the spirit folk who hunt the moon.

"May their arrows stray, their spear-shafts break, their traps all fail to spring!" muttered Ra to himself, for the moon was useful to his tribe. Not only the stars disturbed him; unseen creatures moved in the forest and in the grasses all night long. The echoing tapping of dripping water in the cave had gone, and instead there were the quiet movements of living things going about their business, and hunting each other in the dark. And although he slept, Ra slept so lightly all night long that he dimly knew from the sound and smell of them what creatures had come near. No wolf or wildcat came to startle him awake, but he drowsed on the chill earth till the dawn.

When he woke he went to the stream, and drank

greedily, lifting the water to his mouth in cupped
hands. Cold trickles ran down his forearms, sleeking
the thick hair that had grown upon them last summer.
And when he returned to his hut he had a visitor. Yul
stood there.

"Is there room beside your fire, Ra?" he asked.

"There is no fire yet, but there is room," said Ra.

Yul sat down. "Show me the axe you made at our
fireside last night," he said. Ra stared at Yul in
surprise. Then he picked up the axe, and held it out to
Yul. Yul took it, and turned it over and over in his
hands. Then he held it with the thick end in his palm,
and tried it, striking it against the ground.

"This is a good axe, Ra," he said.

"It is mine," said Ra, puzzled by all this talk of his
axe. "I made it."

"You were quick and deft about making it," said
Yul. "I take longer. And when I have an axe to make,

I gather several stones, so that I need not stop to look for another when the one I am working splits in the wrong place. You had only one stone with you."

"The stones are good to me, Yul. They almost always break as I wish them to."

"Since that is so, Ra, will you make a new spearhead for me? Hard though I try, I cannot make them balance so that the spear flies really straight. You make me a good one."

Ra was silent. This was a new thing Yul was doing; new things frightened Ra. The men of his tribe each did everything for himself. There were no rules for this sort of asking.

"I must hunt, Yul," he said at last. "I am hungry."

"Today I will bring you food. I will hunt until I have enough for two, and share what I catch with you. You can sit here and make me the spear which I need. Do this for me, Ra."

"I will do it," said Ra, unhappily. Indeed one had no choice but to do what Yul wanted; he was big and strong. He could have knocked Ra down with one hand only. Ra did not dare refuse him.

So that morning Ra stood at his door like a woman, watching the men and dogs go out to hunt. The dogs ran yelping at the hunters' heels, and the men walked away into the forest, carrying spears, and bows, and bundles of arrows. The barking sounded clearly in the cold morning, and echoed faintly from the bare hill above the wooded valley. The sounds came more and more distant to Ra's ears. The quiet of the camp made him uneasy. He wanted to run after the hunt, but instead he went looking for a good piece of flint.

He returned to his hut a while later with two large lumps of flint tucked under each arm. Then he sat down and set to work. First he wedged one of his stones firmly on the ground with a little earth, to make an anvil. Then he chose the best of the stones, and taking it in two hands raised it above his head, and brought it hard down on the anvil stone so that it broke cleanly in two across the middle. He took the larger half, and set it down with the new broken surface upwards. And now he took his bone chisel and a spare piece of stone to bang it with. He had to get the slant of the chisel exactly right to make the flint split where he wanted it to. First he struck the stone round the rim of the new surface; and at each blow a flake of stone cracked off the side, so that soon all the hard rough surface of the stone had been struck away, and he was left with a block of pure black, unweathered flint.

Now he worked more carefully still. He struck the top surface of his block near the edge, so that a long narrow flake of flint broke off the side. This flake would make a good knife; Ra put it on one side. Then he tried again, and this time got a shorter, wider chip. Just what he wanted. He put the block aside and

started to work on the chip. It was wafer thin at the edges, and thick in the middle. Ra tapped the edges gently, and broke off little pieces until he had rounded it into a leaf shape. Then he trimmed it, holding a stick at a slant on his anvil, laying the edge of the spearhead against the stick, and pressing the stick upwards under the thin edge of the stone blade until a little flake dropped off. These tiny flakes left a beautiful rippled surface on the flint, like a light wind on dark water. They also left a wavy, bitter-sharp edge. Ra was pleased. He had never made a better one.

But now it was finished he had time to feel hungry. He wondered about the hunt, and felt uneasy. All his instincts, all the ways of his tribe, told him that when he was hungry he must hunt. He shook his head, and took up the long flake of flint he had laid aside before. This had flat straight edges already, because of the way it had split from the block. Ra took careful aim, and sharpened the end of it with a single blow which nicked a diagonal chip from the end. Then he took it, and went up to the forest to cut more brushwood for his hut.

Ra finished his roof, and tied it down securely, and gathered a pile of pebbles for a hearth. All day the women and children stared at him curiously, for it was a new thing for man or boy to stay away from the hunt. And all day Ra's ears were pricked for any sound of the men returning.

At last he heard them. Down the valley, from among the trees, came the sound of singing—a low droning song. The hunt had been good. The hungry families gathered at the hut doors to watch the hunters come. They marched out of the woods, and scrambled up the slope to the camp, bringing the carcasses of deer and rabbits across their shoulders. Ra looked at them hungrily, and licked his lips. He was apprehensive— what if Yul did not keep his unheard-of bargain? The

night would be cold, and the cramps of hunger in his stomach would keep him awake. But Yul brought him the flank of a young doe, and half a rabbit, and exclaimed in delight when he saw the spearhead Ra had made for him.

"This bargain is good," he said.

Ra gathered firewood, and stacked it on his hearth of stones, and went to the Great-grandmother's house to get fire; for all the fires of his tribe were lit from hers, and hers had been carried on torches of pine wood all the way from the winter caves. He roasted his meat on a spit over the fire, not taking long about it, for he liked it still red and raw in the middle. He grunted with pleasure as he sunk his teeth into it, and when he had finished and sat sleepily beside his fire, the good, well-fed feeling spread through his limbs. He just sat enjoying this feeling for a long time, and then he built up his fire so that it would last the night, for it is not only men who hunt for food, and Ra knew that he did not wake quickly when he was not hungry. Then he crept into his hut to sleep. He did not fall asleep at once. He felt odd. Never in all his life before did he remember sleeping well-fed, and yet not tired from running in the hunt all day. But although the strange feeling was a new thing, he liked it.

Ra's new way of life has serious consequences, as you will discover when you read the rest of the book *Toolmaker*. Jill Paton Walsh is an English author with a wide knowledge of historical periods. You may also like another of her books, *Island Sunrise: Prehistoric Cultures in the British Isles*. For another view of the Stone Age, try *The First Farmers in the New Stone Age* by Leonard Weisgard.

I Leave the Island

from *Island of the Blue Dolphins*
by Scott O'Dell

The book from which this story is taken is based on
historical facts. When a ship comes to take a small
band of Indians to the mainland, twelve-year-old
Karana is left behind. She is certain the ship will turn
back for her, but it does not. Except for a pack of wild
dogs, she is alone.

⚜ ⚜ ⚜

Summer is the best time on the Island of the Blue
Dolphins. The sun is warm then and the winds blow
milder out of the west, sometimes out of the south.

It was during these days that the ship might return
and now I spent most of my time on the rock, looking
out from the high headland into the east, toward the
country where my people had gone, across the sea that
was never-ending.

Once while I watched I saw a small object which I
took to be the ship, but a stream of water rose from it
and I knew that it was a whale spouting. During those
summer days I saw nothing else.

The first storm of winter ended my hopes. If the
white men's ship were coming for me it would have
come during the time of good weather. Now I would
have to wait until winter was gone, maybe longer.

The thought of being alone on the island while so
many suns rose from the sea and went slowly back
into the sea filled my heart with loneliness. I had not
felt so lonely before because I was sure that the ship
would return as Matasaip had said it would. Now my
hopes were dead. Now I was really alone. I could not
eat much, nor could I sleep without dreaming terrible
dreams.

The storm blew out of the north, sending big waves
against the island and winds so strong that I was

unable to stay on the rock. I moved my bed to the foot
of the rock and for protection kept a fire going
throughout the night. I slept there five times. The first
night the dogs came and stood outside the ring made
by the fire. I killed three of them with arrows, but not
the leader, and they did not come again.

On the sixth day, when the storm had ended, I went
to the place where the canoes had been hidden, and let
myself down over the cliff. This part of the shore was
sheltered from the wind and I found the canoes just as
they had been left. The dried food was still good, but
the water was stale, so I went back to the spring and
filled a fresh basket.

I had decided during the days of the storm, when I
had given up hope of seeing the ship, that I would take
one of the canoes and go to the country that lay

toward the east. I remember how Kimki, before he had gone, had asked the advice of his ancestors who had lived many ages in the past, who had come to the island from that country, and likewise the advice of Zuma, the medicine man who held power over the wind and the seas. But these things I could not do, for Zuma had been killed by the Aleuts, and in all my life I had never been able to speak with the dead, though many times I had tried.

Yet I cannot say that I was really afraid as I stood there on the shore. I knew that my ancestors had crossed the sea in their canoes, coming from that place which lay beyond. Kimki, too, had crossed the sea. I was not nearly so skilled with a canoe as these men, but I must say that whatever might befall me on the endless waters did not trouble me. It meant far less than the thought of staying on the island alone, without a home or companions, pursued by wild dogs, where everything reminded me of those who were dead and those who had gone away.

Of the four canoes stored there against the cliff, I chose the smallest, which was still very heavy because it could carry six people. The task that faced me was to push it down the rocky shore and into the water, a distance four or five times its length.

This I did by first removing all the large rocks in front of the canoe. I then filled in all these holes with pebbles and along this path laid down long strips of kelp, making a slippery bed. The shore was steep and once I got the canoe to move with its own weight, it slid down the path and into the water.

The sun was in the west when I left the shore. The sea was calm behind the high cliffs. Using the two-bladed paddle I quickly skirted the south part of the island. As I reached the sandspit the wind struck. I was paddling from the back of the canoe because you can go faster kneeling there, but I could not handle it in the wind.

Kneeling in the middle of the canoe, I paddled hard and did not pause until I had gone through the tides that run fast around the sandspit. There were many small waves and I was soon wet, but as I came out from behind the spit the spray lessened and the waves grew long and rolling. Though it would have been easier to go the way they slanted, this would have taken me in the wrong direction. I therefore kept them on my left hand, as well as the island, which grew smaller and smaller, behind me.

At dusk I looked back. The Island of the Blue Dolphins had disappeared. This was the first time that I felt afraid.

There were only hills and valleys of water around me now. When I was in a valley I could see nothing and when the canoe rose out of it, only the ocean stretching away and away.

Night fell and I drank from the basket. The water cooled my throat.

The sea was black and there was no difference between it and the sky. The waves made no sound among themselves, only faint noises as they went under the canoe or struck against it. Sometimes the noises seemed angry and at other times like people laughing. I was not hungry because of my fear.

The first star made me feel less afraid. It came out low in the sky and it was in front of me, toward the east. Other stars began to appear all around, but it was this one I kept my gaze upon. It was in the figure that we call a serpent, a star which shone green and which I knew. Now and then it was hidden by mist, yet it always came out brightly again.

Without this star I would have been lost, for the waves never changed. They came always from the same direction and in a manner that kept pushing me away from the place I wanted to reach. For this reason the canoe made a path in the black water like a snake. But somehow I kept moving toward the star which shone in the east.

This star rose high and then I kept the North Star on my left hand, the one we call "the star that does not move." The wind grew quiet. Since it always died down when the night was half over, I knew how long I had been traveling and how far away the dawn was.

About this time I found that the canoe was leaking. Before dark I had emptied one of the baskets in which food was stored and used it to dip out the water that came over the sides. The water that now moved around my knees was not from the waves.

168

I stopped paddling and worked with the basket until the bottom of the canoe was almost dry. Then I searched around, feeling in the dark along the smooth planks, and found the place near the bow where the water was seeping through a crack as long as my hand and the width of a finger. Most of the time it was out of the sea, but it leaked whenever the canoe dipped forward in the waves.

The places between the planks were filled with black pitch which we gather along the shore. Lacking this, I tore a piece of fiber from my skirt and pressed it into the crack, which held back the water.

Dawn broke in a clear sky and as the sun came out of the waves I saw that it was far off on my left. During the night I had drifted south of the place I wished to go, so I changed my direction and paddled along the path made by the rising sun.

There was no wind on this morning and the long waves went quietly under the canoe. I therefore moved faster than during the night.

I was very tired, but more hopeful than I had been since I left the island. If the good weather did not change I would cover many leagues before dark. Another night and another day might bring me within sight of the shore toward which I was going.

Not long after dawn, while I was thinking of this strange place and what it would look like, the canoe began to leak again. This crack was between the same planks, but was a larger one and close to where I was kneeling.

The fiber I tore from my skirt and pushed into the crack held back most of the water which seeped in whenever the canoe rose and fell with the waves. Yet I could see that the planks were weak from one end to the other, probably from the canoe being stored so long in the sun, and that they might open along their whole length if the waves grew rougher.

It was suddenly clear to me that it was dangerous to go on. The voyage would take two more days, perhaps longer. By turning back to the island I would not have nearly so far to travel.

Still I could not make up my mind to do so. The sea was calm and I had come far. The thought of turning back after all this labor was more than I could bear. Even greater was the thought of the deserted island I would return to, of living there alone and forgotten. For how many suns and how many moons?

The canoe drifted idly on the calm sea while these thoughts went over and over in my mind, but when I saw the water seeping through the crack again, I picked up the paddle. There was no choice except to turn back toward the island.

I knew that only by the best of fortune would I ever reach it.

The wind did not blow until the sun was overhead. Before that time I covered a good distance, pausing only when it was necessary to dip water from the canoe. With the wind I went more slowly and had to stop more often because of the water spilling over the sides, but the leak did not grow worse.

This was my first good fortune. The next was when a swarm of dolphins appeared. They came swimming out of the west, but as they saw the canoe they turned around in a great circle and began to follow me. They swam up slowly and so close that I could see their eyes, which are large and the color of the ocean. Then they swam on ahead of the canoe, crossing back and forth in front of it, diving in and out, as if they were weaving a piece of cloth with their broad snouts.

Dolphins are animals of good omen. It made me happy to have them swimming around the canoe, and though my hands had begun to bleed from the chafing of the paddle, just watching them made me forget the pain. I was very lonely before they appeared, but now I felt that I had friends with me and did not feel the same.

The blue dolphins left me shortly before dusk. They left as quickly as they had come, going on into the west, but for a long time I could see the last of the sun shining on them. After night fell I could still see them in my thoughts and it was because of this that I kept on paddling when I wanted to lie down and sleep.

More than anything, it was the blue dolphins that took me back home.

Fog came with the night, yet from time to time I

could see the star that stands high in the west, the red star called Magat which is part of the figure that looks like a crawfish and is known by that name. The crack in the planks grew wider so I had to stop often to fill it with fiber and to dip out the water.

The night was very long, longer than the night before. Twice I dozed kneeling there in the canoe, though I was more afraid than I had ever been. But the morning broke clear and in front of me lay the dim line of the island like a great fish sunning itself on the sea.

I reached it before the sun was high, the sandspit and its tides that bore me into the shore. My legs were stiff from kneeling and as the canoe struck the sand I fell when I rose to climb out. I crawled through the shallow water and up the beach. There I lay for a long time, hugging the sand in happiness.

I was too tired to think of the wild dogs. Soon I fell asleep. I was awakened by the waves dragging at my

feet. Night had come, but being too tired to leave the sandspit, I crawled to a higher place where I would be safe from the tide, and again went to sleep.

In the morning I found the canoe a short distance away. I took the baskets, my spear, and the bow and arrows, and turned the canoe over so that the tides could not take it out to sea. I then climbed to the headland where I had lived before.

I felt as if I had been gone a long time as I stood there looking down from the high rock. I was happy to be home. Everything that I saw—the otter playing in the kelp, the rings of foam around the rocks that guarded the harbor, the gulls flying, the tides moving past the sandspit—filled me with happiness.

I was surprised that I felt this way, for it was only a short time ago that I had stood on this same rock and felt that I could not bear to live here another day.

I looked out at the blue water stretching away and all the fear I had felt during the time of the voyage came back to me. On the morning I first sighted the island and it had seemed like a great fish sunning itself, I thought that someday I would make the canoe over and go out once more to look for the country that lay beyond the ocean. Now I knew that I would never go again.

The Island of the Blue Dolphins was my home; I had no other.

Will the ship return for Karana? If not, how will a twelve-year-old girl manage to survive on her own? What will she eat? Where will she find shelter? And how will she protect herself from the wild dogs? You can find out by reading the book, *Island of the Blue Dolphins*. Once you start it, you won't be able to put it down. You may also want to try *Call It Courage* by Armstrong Sperry, which is about a Polynesian boy who overcomes his fear of the ocean.

The Nineteenth-Moon-of-Neptune Beasts
by X. J. Kennedy

Who lives on Neptune's nineteenth moon?
How are its ski conditions?
Oh, why have we never heard one word
From the previous expeditions?

We skim low for a look around
And splash down. While untwisting
Our airlock door I catch the sound
Of infant beasts insisting,

"Please, Mom, can't we have something else?
Yes honestly, we've *tried*,
But these screwy eggs with rockets on
Have funny bugs inside!"

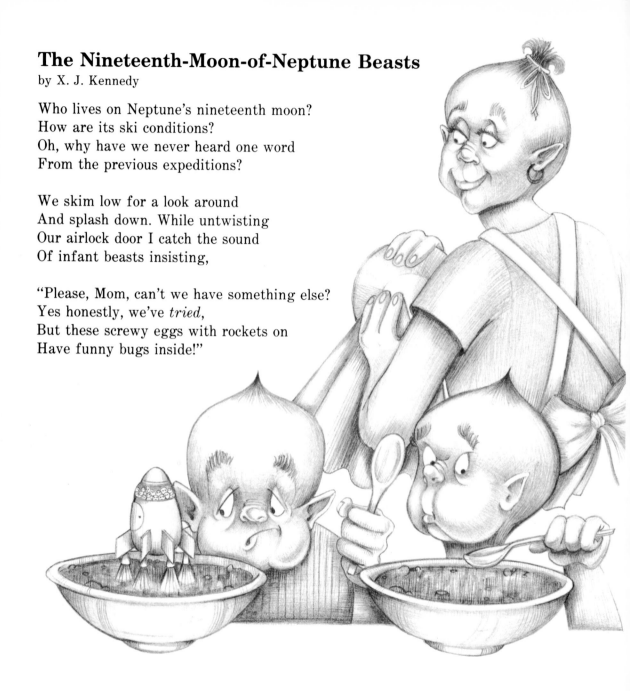

Far Trek
by June Brady

Some things will never change although
We tour out to the stars;
Arriving on the moon we'll find
Our luggage sent to Mars!

Back Yard, July Night
by William Cole

Firefly, airplane, satellite, star—
How I wonder which you are.

There Was a Man
by Dennis Lee

There was a man who never was.
  This tragedy occurred because
His parents, being none too smart,
Were born two hundred years apart.

This Little Pig Built a Spaceship
by Frederick Winsor

This little pig built a spaceship,
  This little pig paid the bill;
This little pig made isotopes,
  This little pig ate a pill;
And this little pig did nothing at all,
  But he's just a little pig still.

The Difficulty of Living on Other Planets
by Dennis Lee

A Martian with a mangled spear
  Is stuffing tarts in my left ear.
If I turn off my hearing aid
  Will I still taste the marmalade?

The Boy Who Became a Wizard

from *A Wizard of Earthsea*
by Ursula K. Le Guin

Earthsea is an imaginary world made up entirely of islands. On one of these, the island of Gont, lives the boy Duny. Duny longs to be a mage, or wizard, and he already has some magical powers. Now his magic is about to be put to the test. The savage Kargs, from the Kargad Empire which lies to the west, have sailed to invade Gont.

⚜ ⚜ ⚜

In those days the Kargad Empire was strong. Those are four great lands that lie between the Northern and the Eastern Reaches: Karego-At, Atuan, Hur-at-Hur, Atnini. The tongue they speak there is not like any spoken in the Archipelago or the other Reaches, and they are a savage people, white-skinned, yellow-haired, and fierce, liking the sight of blood and the smell of burning towns. Last year they had attacked the Torikles and the strong island Torheven, raiding in

great force in fleets of red-sailed ships. News of this came north to Gont, but the Lords of Gont were busy with their piracy and paid small heed to the woes of other lands. Then Spevy fell to the Kargs and was looted and laid waste, its people taken as slaves, so that even now it is an isle of ruins. In lust of conquest the Kargs sailed next to Gont, coming in a host, thirty great long ships, to East Port. They fought through that town, took it, burned it; leaving their ships under guard at the mouth of the River Ar they went up the Vale wrecking and looting, slaughtering cattle and men. As they went they split into bands, and each of these bands plundered where it chose. Fugitives brought warning to the villages of the heights. Soon the people of Ten Alders saw smoke darken the eastern sky, and that night those who climbed the High Fall looked down on the Vale all hazed and red-streaked with fires where fields ready for harvest had been set ablaze, and orchards burned, the fruit roasting on the blazing boughs, and barns and farmhouses smouldered in ruin.

Some of the villagers fled up the ravines and hid in the forest, and some made ready to fight for their lives, and some did neither but stood about lamenting. The witch was one who fled, hiding alone in a cave up on the Kapperding Scarp and sealing the cave-mouth with spells. Duny's father the bronzesmith was one who stayed, for he would not leave his smelting-pit and forge where he had worked for fifty years. All that night he labored beating up what ready metal he had there into spearpoints, and others worked with him binding these to the handles of hoes and rakes, there being no time to make sockets and shaft them properly. There had been no weapons in the village but hunting bows and short knives, for the mountain folk of Gont are not warlike; it is not warriors they are famous for, but goat-thieves, sea-pirates, and wizards.

With sunrise came a thick white fog, as on many autumn mornings in the heights of the island. Among their huts and houses down the straggling street of Ten Alders the villagers stood waiting with their hunting bows and new-forged spears, not knowing whether the Kargs might be far off or very near, all silent, all peering into the fog that hid shapes and distances and dangers from their eyes.

With them was Duny. He had worked all night at the forge-bellows, pushing and pulling the two long sleeves of goathide that fed the fire with a blast of air. Now his arms so ached and trembled from that work that he could not hold out the spear he had chosen. He did not see how he could fight or be of any good to himself or the villagers. It rankled at his heart that he should die, spitted on a Kargish lance, while still a boy: that he should go into the dark land without ever having known his own name, his true name as a man. He looked down at his thin arms, wet with cold fog-dew, and raged at his weakness, for he knew his strength. There was power in him, if he knew how to use it, and he sought among all the spells he knew for some device that might give him and his companions an advantage, or at least a chance. But need alone is not enough to set power free: there must be knowledge.

The fog was thinning now under the heat of the sun that shone bare above on the peak in a bright sky. As the mists moved and parted in great drifts and smoky wisps, the villagers saw a band of warriors coming up the mountain. They were armored with bronze helmets and greaves and breastplates of heavy leather and shields of wood and bronze, and armed with swords and the long Kargish lance. Winding up along the steep bank of the Ar they came in a plumed, clanking, straggling line, near enough already that their white faces could be seen, and the words of their jargon heard as they shouted to one another. In this band of the invading horde there were about a hundred men, which is not many; but in the village were only eighteen men and boys.

Now need called knowledge out: Duny, seeing the
fog blow and thin across the path before the Kargs,
saw a spell that might avail him. An old
weatherworker of the Vale, seeking to win the boy as
prentice, had taught him several charms. One of these
tricks was called fogweaving, a binding-spell that
gathers the mists together for a while in one place;
with it one skilled in illusion can shape the mist into
fair ghostly seemings, which last a little and fade
away. The boy had no such skill, but his intent was
different, and he had the strength to turn the spell
into his own ends. Rapidly and aloud he named the
places of the boundaries of the village, and then spoke
the fogweaving charm, but in among its words he
enlaced the words of a spell of concealment, and last
he cried the word that set the magic going.

Even as he did so his father coming up behind him
struck him hard on the side of the head, knocking him
right down. "Be still, fool! keep your blattering mouth
shut, and hide if you can't fight!"

Duny got to his feet. He could hear the Kargs now
at the end of the village, as near as the great yew tree

by the tanner's yard. Their voices were clear, and the clink and creak of their harness and arms, but they could not be seen. The fog had closed and thickened all over the village, greying the light, blurring the world till a man could hardly see his own hands before him.

"I've hidden us all," Duny said, sullenly, for his head hurt from his father's blow, and the working of the doubled incantation had drained his strength. "I'll keep up this fog as long as I can. Get the others to lead them up the High Fall."

The smith stared at his son who stood wraithlike in that weird, dank mist. It took him a minute to see Duny's meaning, but when he did he ran at once, noiselessly, knowing every fence and corner of the village, to find the others and tell them what to do. Now through the grey fog bloomed a blur of red, and the Kargs set fire to the thatch of a house. Still they

did not come up into the village, but waited at the lower end till the mist should lift and lay bare their loot and prey.

The tanner, whose house it was that burned, sent a couple of boys skipping right under the Kargs' noses, taunting and yelling and vanishing again like smoke into smoke. Meantime the older men, creeping behind fences and running from house to house, came close on the other side and sent a volley of arrows and spears at the warriors, who stood all in a bunch. One Karg fell writhing with a spear, still warm from its forging, right through his body. Others were arrow-bitten, and all enraged. They charged forward then to hew down their puny attackers, but they found only the fog about them, full of voices. They followed the voices, stabbing ahead into the mist with their great, plumed, bloodstained lances. Up the length of the street they

came shouting, and never knew they had run right through the village, as the empty huts and houses loomed and disappeared again in the writhing grey fog. The villagers ran scattering, most of them keeping well ahead since they knew the ground; but some, boys or old men, were slow. The Kargs stumbling on them drove their lances or hacked with their swords, yelling their war cry, the names of the White Godbrothers of Atuan: "Wuluah! Atwah!"

Some of the band stopped when they felt the land grow rough underfoot, but others pressed right on, seeking the phantom village, following dim wavering shapes that fled just out of reach before them. All the mist had come alive with these fleeing forms, dodging, flickering, fading on every side. One group of the Kargs chased the wraiths straight to the High Fall, the cliff's edge above the springs of Ar, and the shapes they pursued ran out onto the air and there vanished in a thinning of the mist, while the pursuers fell screaming through fog and sudden sunlight a hundred feet sheer to the shallow pools among the rocks. And those that came behind and did not fall stood at the cliff's edge, listening.

Now dread came into the Kargs' hearts and they began to seek one another, not the villagers, in the uncanny mist. They gathered on the hillside, and yet always there were wraiths and ghost-shapes among them, and other shapes that ran and stabbed from behind with spear or knife and vanished again. The Kargs began to run, all of them, downhill, stumbling, silent, until all at once they ran out from the grey blind mist and saw the river and the ravines below the village all bare and bright in morning sunlight. Then they stopped, gathering together, and looked back. A wall of wavering, writhing grey lay blank across the path, hiding all that lay behind it. Out from it burst two or three stragglers, lunging and stumbling along, their long lances rocking on their shoulders. Not one

Karg looked back more than that once. All went down, in haste, away from the enchanted place.

Farther down the Northward Vale those warriors got their fill of fighting. The towns of the East Forest, from Ovark to the coast, had gathered their men and sent them against the invaders of Gont. Band after band they came down from the hills, and that day and the next the Kargs were harried back down to the beaches above East Port, where they found their ships burnt; so they fought with their backs to the sea till every man of them was killed, and the sands of Armouth were brown with blood until the tide came in.

But on that morning in Ten Alders village and up on the High Fall, the dank grey fog had clung a while, and then suddenly it blew and drifted and melted away. This man and that stood up in the windy brightness of the morning, and looked about him wondering. Here lay a dead Karg with yellow hair long, loose, and bloody; there lay the village tanner, killed in battle like a king.

Down in the village the house that had been set afire still blazed. They ran to put the fire out, since their battle had been won. In the street, near the great yew, they found Duny the bronzesmith's son standing by himself, bearing no hurt, but speechless and stupid like one stunned. They were well aware of what he had done, and they led him into his father's house and went calling for the witch to come down out of her cave and heal the lad who had saved their lives and their property, all but four who were killed by the Kargs, and the one house that was burnt.

No weapon-hurt had come to the boy, but he would not speak nor eat nor sleep; he seemed not to hear what was said to him, not to see those who came to see him. There was none in those parts wizard enough to cure what ailed him. His aunt said, "He has overspent his power," but she had no art to help him.

While he lay thus dark and dumb, the story of the lad who wove the fog and scared off Kargish

swordsmen with a mess of shadows was told all down
the Northward Vale, and in the East Forest, and high
on the mountain and over the mountain even in the
Great Port of Gont. So it happened that on the fifth
day after the slaughter at Armouth a stranger came
into Ten Alders village, a man neither young nor old,
who came cloaked and bareheaded, lightly carrying a
great staff of oak that was as tall as himself. He did
not come up the course of the Ar like most people, but
down, out of the forests of the higher mountainside.
The village goodwives saw well that he was a wizard,
and when he told them that he was a heal-all, they
brought him straight to the smith's house. Sending
away all but the boy's father and aunt the stranger
stooped above the cot where Duny lay staring into the
dark, and did no more than lay his hand on the boy's
forehead and touch his lips once.

Duny sat up slowly looking about him. In a little
while he spoke, and strength and hunger began to
come back into him. They gave him a little to drink
and eat, and he lay back again, always watching the
stranger with dark wondering eyes.

The bronzesmith said to that stranger, "You are no
common man."

"Nor will this boy be a common man," the other
answered. "The tale of his deed with the fog has come
to Re Albi, which is my home. I have come here to give
him his name, if as they say he has not yet made his
passage into manhood."

The witch whispered to the smith, "Brother, this
must surely be the Mage of Re Albi, Ogion the Silent,
that one who tamed the earthquake—"

"Sir," said the bronzesmith who would not let a
great name daunt him, "my son will be thirteen this
month coming, but we thought to hold his Passage at
the feast of Sun-return this winter."

"Let him be named as soon as may be," said the

mage, "for he needs his name. I have other business now, but I will come back here for the day you choose. If you see fit I will take him with me when I go thereafter. And if he prove apt I will keep him as prentice, or see to it that he is schooled as fits his gifts. For to keep dark the mind of the mageborn, that is a dangerous thing."

Very gently Ogion spoke, but with certainty, and even the hard-headed smith assented to all he said.

On the day the boy was thirteen years old, a day in the early splendor of autumn while still the bright leaves are on the trees, Ogion returned to the village from his rovings over Gont Mountain, and the ceremony of Passage was held. The witch took from the boy his name Duny, the name his mother had given him as a baby. Nameless and naked he walked into the cold springs of the Ar where it rises among rocks under the high cliffs. As he entered the water clouds crossed the sun's face and great shadows slid and mingled over the water of the pool about him. He crossed to the far bank, shuddering with cold but walking slow and erect as he should through that icy, living water. As he came to the bank Ogion, waiting, reached out his hand and clasping the boy's arm whispered to him his true name: Ged.

Thus was he given his name by one very wise in the uses of power.

The feasting was far from over, and all the villagers were making merry with plenty to eat and beer to drink and a chanter from down the Vale singing the *Deed of the Dragonlords*, when the mage spoke in his quiet voice to Ged: "Come, lad. Bid your people farewell and leave them feasting."

Ged fetched what he had to carry, which was the good bronze knife his father had forged him, and a leather coat the tanner's widow had cut down to his size, and an alderstick his aunt had becharmed for him:

that was all he owned besides his shirt and breeches.
He said farewell to them, all the people he knew in all
the world, and looked about once at the village that
straggled and huddled there under the cliffs, over the
river-springs. Then he set off with his new master
through the steep slanting forests of the mountain isle,
through the leaves and shadows of bright autumn.

In the book, *The Wizard of Earthsea*, you can follow
Ged to the School for Wizards. You will also see what
happens when, driven by pride and jealousy, he uses
his power too soon and unleashes a shadowy evil that
threatens all of Earthsea. The author, Ursula K. Le
Guin, has written two other books about the
adventures of Ged that you will want to read: *Tombs
of Atuan* and *The Farthest Shore*.

Jabberwocky

by Lewis Carroll

'Twas brillig, and the slithy toves
  Did gyre and gimble in the wabe:
All mimsy were the borogoves,
  And the mome raths outgrabe.

"Beware the Jabberwock, my son!
  The jaws that bite, the claws that catch!
Beware the Jubjub bird, and shun
  The frumious Bandersnatch!"

He took his vorpal sword in hand:
  Long time the manxome foe he sought—
So rested he by the Tumtum tree,
  And stood awhile in thought.

And, as in uffish thought he stood,
  The Jabberwock, with eyes of flame,
Came whiffling through the tulgey wood,
  And burbled as it came!

One, two! One, two! And through and through
  The vorpal blade went snicker-snack!
He left it dead, and with its head
  He went galumphing back.

"And hast thou slain the Jabberwock?
  Come to my arms, my beamish boy!
O frabjous day! Callooh! Callay!"
  He chortled in his joy.

'Twas brillig, and the slithy toves
  Did gyre and gimble in the wabe:
All mimsy were the borogoves,
  And the mome raths outgrabe.

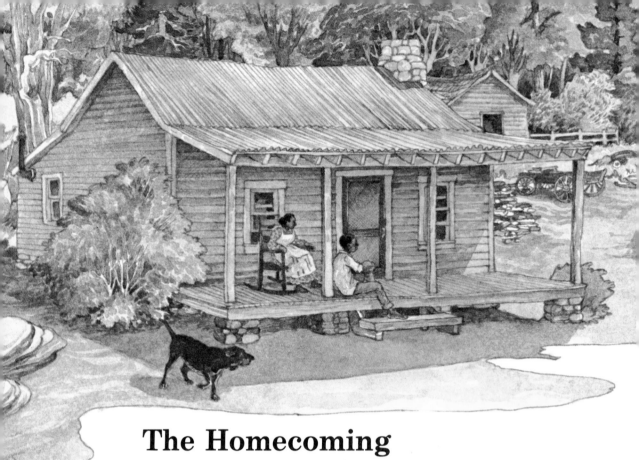

The Homecoming

from *Sounder*
by William H. Armstrong

Sounder, a fine coon dog, was shot when the sheriff
arrested his master. His wounds have healed, but he is
badly crippled. With the care of the boy—his master's
son—and the boy's mother, he has lived for many
years. But he can't forget his master, who has never
returned.

❧ ❧ ❧

Late one August afternoon the boy and his mother sat
on the shaded corner of the porch. The heat and
drought of dog days had parched the earth, and the
crops had been laid by. The boy had come home early
because there was nothing to do in the fields.

"Dog days is a terrible time," the woman said. "It's
when the heat is so bad the dogs go mad." The boy
would not tell her that the teacher had told him that

dog days got their name from the Dog Star because it rose and set with the sun during that period. She had her own feeling for the earth, he thought, and he would not confuse it.

"It sure is hot," he said instead. "Lucky to come from the fields early." He watched the heat waves as they made the earth look like it was moving in little ripples.

Sounder came around the corner of the cabin from somewhere, hobbled back and forth as far as the road several times, and then went to his cool spot under the porch. "That's what I say about dog days," the woman said. "Poor creature's been addled with the heat for three days. Can't find no place to quiet down. Been down the road nearly out o' sight a second time today, and now he musta come from the fencerows. Whines all the time. A mad dog is a fearful sight. Slobberin' at the mouth and runnin' every which way 'cause they're blind. Have to shoot 'em 'fore they bite some child. It's awful hard."

"Sounder won't go mad," the boy said. "He's lookin' for a cooler spot, I reckon."

A lone figure came on the landscape as a speck and slowly grew into a ripply form through the heat waves. "Scorchin' to be walkin' and totin' far today," she said as she pointed to the figure on the road.

A catbird fussed in the wilted lilac at the corner of the cabin. "Why's that bird fussin' when no cat's prowlin'? Old folks has a sayin' that if a catbird fusses 'bout nothin', somethin' bad is comin'. It's a bad sign."

"Sounder, I reckon," the boy said. "He just passed her bush when he came around the cabin."

In the tall locust at the edge of the fence, its top leaves yellowed from lack of water, a mockingbird mimicked the catbird with half a dozen notes, decided it was too hot to sing, and disappeared. The great coon dog, whose rhythmic panting came through the porch floor, came from under the house and began to whine.

As the figure on the road drew near, it took shape and grew indistinct again in the wavering heat. Sometimes it seemed to be a person dragging something, for little puffs of red dust rose in sulfurous clouds at every other step. Once or twice they thought it might be a brown cow or mule, dragging its hooves in the sand and raising and lowering its weary head.

Sounder panted faster, wagged his tail, whined, moved from the dooryard to the porch and back to the dooryard.

The figure came closer. Now it appeared to be a child carrying something on its back and limping.

"The children still at the creek?" she asked.

"Yes, but it's about dry."

Suddenly the voice of the great coon hound broke the sultry August deadness. The dog dashed along the road, leaving three-pointed clouds of red dust to settle back to earth behind him. The mighty voice rolled out upon the valley, each flutelike bark echoing from slope to slope.

"Lord's mercy! Dog days done made him mad." And the rocker was still.

Sounder was a young dog again. His voice was the same mellow sound that had ridden the November breeze from the lowlands to the hills. The boy and his mother looked at each other. The catbird stopped her fussing in the wilted lilac bush. On three legs, the dog moved with the same lightning speed that had carried him to the throat of a grounded raccoon.

Sounder's master had come home. Taking what might have been measured as a halting half step and then pulling a stiff, dead leg forward, dragging a foot turned sideways in the dust, the man limped into the yard. Sounder seemed to understand that to jump up and put his paw against his master's breast would topple him into the dust, so the great dog smelled and whined and wagged his tail and licked the limp hand dangling at his master's side. He hopped wildly around his master in a circle that almost brought head and tail together.

The head of the man was pulled to the side where a limp arm dangled and where the foot pointed outward as it was dragged through the dust. What had been a shoulder was now pushed up and back to make a one-sided hump so high that the leaning head seemed to rest upon it. The mouth was askew too, and the voice came out of the part farthest away from the withered, wrinkled, lifeless side.

The woman in the still rocker said, "Lord, Lord," and sat suffocated in shock.

"Sounder knew it was you just like you was comin' home from work," the boy said in a clear voice.

Half the voice of the man was gone too, so in slow,

measured, stuttering he told how he had been caught in a dynamite blast in the prison quarry, how the dead side had been crushed under an avalanche of limestone, and how he had been missed for a whole night in the search for dead and wounded. He told how the pain of the crushing stone had stopped in the night, how doctors had pushed and pulled and encased the numb side of his body in a cast, how they had spoken kindly to him and told him he would die. But he resolved he would not die, even with a half-dead body, because he wanted to come home again.

"For being hurt, they let me have time off my sentence," the man said, "and since I couldn't work, I guess they was glad to."

"The Lord has brought you home," the woman said.

The boy heard faint laughter somewhere behind the cabin. The children were coming home from the creek. He went around the cabin slowly, then hurried to meet them.

"Pa's home," he said and grabbed his sister, who had started to run toward the cabin. "Wait. He's mighty crippled up, so behave like nothin' has happened."

"Can he walk?" the youngest child asked.

"Yes! And don't you ask no questions."

"You been mighty natural and considerate," the mother said to the younger children later when she went to the woodpile and called them to pick dry kindling for a quick fire. When she came back to the porch she said, "We was gonna just have a cold piece 'cause it's so sultry, but now I think I'll cook."

Everything don't change much, the boy thought. There's eatin' and sleepin' and talkin' and settin' that goes on. One day might be different from another, but there ain't much difference when they're put together.

Sometimes there were long quiet spells. Once or twice the boy's mother said to the boy, "He's powerful proud of your learnin'. Read somethin' from the

Scriptures." But mostly they just talked about heat and cold, and wind and clouds, and what's gonna be done, and time passing.

As the days of August passed and September brought signs of autumn, the crippled man sat on the porch step and leaned the paralyzed, deformed side of his body against a porch post. This was the only comfortable sitting position he could find. The old coon dog would lie facing his master, with his one eye fixed and his one ear raised. Sometimes he would tap his tail against the earth. Sometimes the ear would droop and the eye would close. Then the great muscles would flex in dreams of the hunt, and the mighty chest would give off a muffled whisper of a bark. Sometimes the two limped together to the edge of the fields, or wandered off into the pine woods. They never went along the road. Perhaps they knew how strange a picture they made when they walked together.

About the middle of September the boy left to go back to his teacher. "It's the most important thing," his mother said.

And the crippled man said, "We're fine. We won't need nothin'."

"I'll come for a few days before it's cold to help gather wood and walnuts."

The broken body of the old man withered more and more, but when the smell of harvest and the hunt came with October, his spirit seemed to quicken his dragging step. One day he cleaned the dusty lantern globe, and the old dog, remembering, bounced on his three legs and wagged his tail as if to say "I'm ready."

The boy had come home. To gather the felled trees and chop the standing dead ones was part of the field pay too. He had been cutting and dragging timber all day.

Sometimes he had looked longingly at the lantern and possum sack, but something inside him had said

"Wait. Wait and go together." But the boy did not want to go hunting anymore. And without his saying anything, his father had said, "You're too tired, child. We ain't goin' far, no way."

In the early darkness the halting, hesitant swing of the lantern marked the slow path from fields to pine woods toward the lowlands. The boy stood on the porch, watching until the light was lost behind pine branches. Then he went and sat by the stove. His mother rocked as the mound of kernels grew in the fold of her apron. "He been mighty peart," she said. "I hope he don't fall in the dark. Maybe he'll be happy now he can go hunting again." And she took up her singing where she had left off.

> *Ain't nobody else gonna walk it for you,*
> *You gotta walk it by yourself.*

Sounder, his master, the boy, and the boy's mother all have the kind of courage it takes to live through long, hard years. And that courage helps to bring about some very important changes in the boy's life. To find out what they are, read *Sounder*. You'll meet a very different kind of dog in *Good-Bye, My Lady* by James Street. The "lady" washes herself like a cat, laughs like a child, and becomes a most unusual friend for Skeeter, the boy who finds her.

Requiem
by Robert Louis Stevenson

Under the wide and starry sky
Dig the grave and let me lie.
Glad did I live and gladly die,
  And I laid me down with a will.

This be the verse you grave for me:
Here he lies where he longed to be;
Home is the sailor, home from sea,
  And the hunter home from the hill.

Macavity: The Mystery Cat

by T. S. Eliot

Macavity's a Mystery Cat: he's called the Hidden Paw—
For he's the master criminal who can defy the Law.
He's the bafflement of Scotland Yard, the Flying Squad's despair:
For when they reach the scene of crime—*Macavity's not there!*

Macavity, Macavity, there's no one like Macavity,
He's broken every human law, he breaks the law of gravity.
His powers of levitation would make a fakir stare,
And when you reach the scene of crime—*Macavity's not there!*
You may seek him in the basement, you may look up in the air—
But I tell you once and once again, *Macavity's not there!*

Macavity's a ginger cat, he's very tall and thin;
You would know him if you saw him, for his eyes are sunken in.
His brow is deeply lined with thought, his head is highly domed;
His coat is dusty from neglect, his whiskers are uncombed.

He sways his head from side to side, with movements like a snake;
And when you think he's half asleep, he's always wide awake.
Macavity, Macavity, there's no one like Macavity,
For he's a fiend in feline shape, a monster of depravity.
You may meet him in a by-street, you may see him in the square—
But when a crime's discovered, then *Macavity's not there!*

He's outwardly respectable. (They say he cheats at cards.)
And his footprints are not found in any file of Scotland Yard's.
And when the larder's looted, or the jewel-case is rifled,
Or when the milk is missing, or another Peke's been stifled,
Or the greenhouse glass is broken, and the trellis past repair—
Ay, there's the wonder of the thing! *Macavity's not there!*

And when the Foreign Office find a Treaty's gone astray,
Or the Admiralty lose some plans and drawings by the way,
There may be a scrap of paper in the hall or on the stair—
But it's useless to investigate—*Macavity's not there!*
And when the loss has been disclosed, the Secret Service say:
"It *must* have been Macavity!"—but he's a mile away.
You'll be sure to find him resting, or a-licking of his thumbs,
Or engaged in doing complicated long division sums.

Macavity, Macavity, there's no one like Macavity,
There never was a Cat of such deceitfulness and suavity.
He always has an alibi, and one or two to spare:
At whatever time the deed took place—MACAVITY WASN'T THERE!
And they say that all the Cats whose wicked deeds are widely known,
(I might mention Mungojerrie, I might mention Griddlebone)
Are nothing more than agents for the Cat who all the time
Just controls their operations: the Napoleon of Crime!

How It Snowed Fur
and Rained Fry Cakes
in Western Virginia

from *The Remarkable History of Tony Beaver—*
West Virginian by Mary E. Cober

This story is a special kind of American folk tale
called a tall tale. Tall tales are a lot of fun because
they are full of whopping lies that are told in what
seems to be a truthful way—as you will find out when
you read this tale about Tony Beaver.

❧ ❧ ❧

One day Tony heard that a school had been started
over in the next valley. Never having been in a school,
Tony was anxious to see what one looked like. Early
one morning he set out to walk the twenty miles to
take a look.

Tony found he liked school right well. He found that
by stretching his legs a little more than usual, he could
soon take some mighty big steps. Before he was
through, he could take a step of almost a quarter of a
mile. Along with finding a few short cuts, Tony was
able to get to school in jig time.

One day when he was moseying to school, he saw
two big mountain lions—he called them painters—one
on each side of the path. "They'll be looking for trouble
and I don't want to be it," Tony thought. Then he had
an idea. "Sic 'em! Sic 'em!" he cried.

Immediately the two big cats flew at each other. As
they tussled they kept jumping higher and higher.
Soon they were jumping as high as Tony's head.

"Sic 'em! Sic 'em!" Tony yelled again.

This time the two painters jumped as high as the
trees and fought harder than ever.

After school Tony used the same path, keeping a
sharp eye out for the painters. They were not to be

seen but as he drew near the place where he had seen them last, bits of fur began to float down from the sky. "That's strange," thought Tony. "Where can this be coming from?"

Tony looked all around and then saw a fleecy cloud from which the fur seemed to be coming. "Why, those painters have jumped so high that they landed in the clouds," he cried.

And that's exactly what happened. And *that's* the time it snowed fur in western Virginia.

Tony found that his trips to school resulted in many interesting experiences. One day his granny, who was visiting them for a spell, made some fry cakes, or doughnuts as you would probably call them. She made so many that even the hearty-eating Beavers couldn't finish them all. Tony took along a sack to school for the teacher.

Now on the way Tony met Brer Rabbit who had come to pay his Virginia cousins a visit. Tony was munching a doughnut and this made Brer Rabbit very hungry; so he decided to get all of the fry cakes for himself.

"Hi, Big Boy," greeted Brer Rabbit. "What you got there?"

"Fry cakes," Tony answered politely. "Have one?"

"Well, don't mind if I do. Say, I know some magic words that will make these fry cakes multiply and then there will be lots for both of us."

"What are the words?" Tony asked.

"First, you must put the fry cakes on that tree stump, and then close your eyes. After that I'll tell you the magic words."

Tony did as directed, only he didn't close his eyes tight. When he saw Brer Rabbit reach for the cakes, Tony's toe reached for Brer Rabbit and he kicked him sky high into the air. And *that's* the time it rained fry cakes for three days over all of western Virginia.

You see, even as a young'un, Tony Beaver was hard to beat.

Tony Beaver is only one of many heroes in a host of
American tall tales. Others are Paul Bunyan, Captain
Stormalong, Mike Fink, and Pecos Bill. You can read
about them in such books as *Yankee Doodle's Cousins*
by Anne Malcolmson and *Heroes in American Folklore*
by Irwin Shapiro.

Myths of Ancient Greece

from *Stories of the Gods and Heroes*
by Sally Benson

Myths are the wonderful tales that people long ago
told about their gods and heroes—tales that still
fascinate people today. Here are two Greek myths
that are more than two thousand years old. The first
myth tells about one of the adventures of Theseus, a
hero who performed many great deeds. The other is
the story of a man who was neither a god nor a hero,
but who struggled to fly.

Theseus and the Minotaur

Theseus was the son of Aegeus, king of Athens, and of
Aethra, daughter of the king of Troezen. He was
brought up at Troezen, and when he reached the age of
manhood was to proceed to Athens and present himself
to his father. Before his son's birth, Aegeus had placed
his own sword and shoes under a large stone and told
his wife to send his son to him when he became strong
enough to roll away the stone and take the sword and
shoes from under it. When she thought that the time
had come, his mother led Theseus to the stone, and he
rolled it aside with ease.

As the roads were infested with robbers, his
grandfather, the king of Troezen, urged him earnestly
to take the shorter and safer way to his father's
country, which was to go by sea. But the youth, feeling
in himself the spirit and soul of a hero, was eager to
emulate Hercules,[1] with whose fame all Greece then
rang. He wished to destroy the evildoers and monsters
that oppressed the country, and determined to take the
more perilous and adventurous journey by land.

---

1. Hercules is the Roman name for the Greek hero Heracles. He was
famous for his strength and performed many great deeds.

His first day's journey brought him to Epidaurus where Periphetes dwelt, the son of Vulcan.[2] This ferocious savage always went about armed with a club of iron, and all travelers stood in terror of his violence. When he saw Theseus approach, he set upon him viciously, but he soon fell beneath the blows of the young hero, who took possession of his club and carried it ever afterwards as a memento of his first victory.

Several similar contests with the petty tyrants and marauders of the country followed, in all of which Theseus was victorious. One of these monsters was called Procrustes or the Stretcher. He had an iron bedstead on which he tied all travelers who fell into his hands. If they were shorter than the bed, he stretched their limbs to make them fit it; if they were longer than the bed, he cut off their feet. Theseus tied him to the bed and cut off his head to make him fit it.

Having overcome all the perils of the road, Theseus reached Athens at last, where new dangers awaited him. Medea,[3] the sorceress who had fled from Corinth

2. Vulcan is the Roman name for Hephaestus, the Greek god of fire.
3. Medea was a sorceress who helped Jason win the Golden Fleece—the wool of a golden ram.

after her separation from Jason,[4] had become the wife of Aegeus, the father of Theseus. Knowing by her magic arts who Theseus was, and fearing the loss of her influence with her husband if Theseus should be acknowledged as his son, she filled the mind of Aegeus with suspicions of the young stranger. She whispered to Aegeus that the youth had come to poison him, and that he, in turn, should administer a cup of poison to Theseus. But when Theseus stepped forward to take the cup, Aegeus caught sight of his own sword hanging at the hero's side. Striking the fatal cup to the floor, he embraced the boy and called upon everyone to witness that he had found his son. Medea, once more detected in her villainies, fled the country and went to Asia, where the country afterwards called Medea received its name from her.

The Athenians were at that time in deep affliction on account of the tribute which they were forced to pay to Minos, king of Crete. Every year seven youths and seven maidens were sent to be devoured by the Minotaur, a monster with a bull's body and a human

---

4. Jason was a Greek hero who led a band of men called the Argonauts on the dangerous quest for the Golden Fleece.

head.[5] It was a horrid beast, strong and fierce, and was kept in a labyrinth which had been constructed by Daedalus, a skilled craftsman. The labyrinth was so artfully designed that whoever entered it could never find his way out unassisted. Paths led into paths, and all of them seemingly led nowhere. Here the Minotaur roamed and was fed with human victims.

Every year when the time came for the youths and maidens to be delivered to the monster, the country was plunged into mourning. Mothers trembled lest their beautiful daughters or brave sons should be chosen to feed the dreadful creature, and the houses of the entire populace were draped in black as the procession of young people bravely set out for the labyrinth.

When Theseus arrived in Athens, the time was approaching for the sacrifice. He noticed the sad faces of the people of the city and asked his father to tell him the cause of their sorrow. Aegeus reluctantly told him the story. Theseus, indignant at the cruel and useless sacrifice, resolved to deliver his countrymen from the calamity or die in the attempt. The youths and maidens were drawn by lot every year, but Theseus, in spite of the entreaties of his father, offered himself as one of the victims.

The morning for their departure dawned, and Theseus joined the weeping, shivering group. They were dressed in deep black, but Theseus had arrayed himself in gay colors, confident of victory. The ship which was to carry them to their destination had black sails, and Theseus promised his father that he would change the sails to white if he returned victorious.

When they arrived in Crete, the youths and maidens were exhibited before Minos, and Ariadne, the daughter of the king, saw Theseus and fell in love with

---

5. In other tales, the Minotaur is described as having the head of a bull and the body of a man.

him. She furnished him with a sword and with a spool of thread. She instructed him to fasten the thread to a stone as he entered the labyrinth and unwind it as he made his way into the maze, keeping it firmly grasped in his hand so that he could guide himself back to the daylight once more.

Cheered by these gifts, the young people entered the dark, wet caves. They clung together while Theseus fastened the thread securely to a jutting rock, and then, walking one behind the other, they followed the first path. Around and around they traveled, their ears alert for the slightest sound which would warn them of the approach of the monster. It was pitch dark, and Theseus was careful of the thread lest it catch on a sharp corner and break off. They wandered for hours, too cold and frightened to sit down. Their eyes became accustomed to the darkness and they could make out the tall grey walls and hundreds of paths winding in the half-light. There was an odor of decay in the air, and they saw the white bones of the victims of other years lying on the ground.

Suddenly, they heard a tremendous bellowing and the stamping of angry feet. It was the Minotaur, ravenous from his year's fast, and anxious to partake of the sweet blood of the youths and maidens. At the sound, there were screams of horror from the victims. Theseus begged them to be calm and, ordering them to a place of comparative safety in the rocks, he advanced alone to meet the Minotaur. He saw the monster's head as it turned the corner. Its beard was caked with the blood of years. Its mouth dripped in anticipation of the feast that awaited it. It uttered wild cries which resembled the bellowings of a bull and the roars of an insane human. As it caught sight of Theseus, it galloped forward ready to crunch him in its powerful jaws, trample him with its cloven hoofs, and devour him.

With one quick movement, Theseus stepped forward
and plunged his sword into the creature's breast.
Maddened, the Minotaur reared and would have
brought its feet down on Theseus's head, had not the
hero ducked and stabbed him time and time again.
When the monster lay dead, the young people threw
their arms around one another in a frenzy of joy.
Following the precious thread, they made their way
out of the labyrinth.

They silently crept to their ship which lay in the
harbor, and, with Ariadne, set sail for Athens. On their
way home, they stopped at the island of Naxos where
Theseus dreamed that Minerva appeared to him and
commanded him to abandon Ariadne. He awoke and
roused his companions, leaving Ariadne asleep on the
island.

On approaching the coast of Attica, Theseus forgot
the signal and neglected to raise the white sails.
Aegeus, thinking his son had perished, put an end to
his own life. Thus, Theseus became king of Athens.

The Flight of Icarus

When Theseus escaped from the labyrinth, King Minos
flew into a rage with its builder, Daedalus, and
ordered him shut up in a high tower that faced the
lonely sea. In time, with the help of his young son,
Icarus, Daedalus managed to escape from the tower,
only to find himself a prisoner on the island. Several
times he tried by bribery to stow away on one of the
vessels sailing from Crete, but King Minos kept strict
watch over them, and no ships were allowed to sail
without being carefully searched.

Daedalus was an ingenious artist and was not
discouraged by his failures. "Minos may control the
land and sea," he said, "but he does not control the air.
I will try that way."

He called his son Icarus to him and told the boy to
gather up all the feathers he could find on the rocky
shore. As thousands of gulls soared over the island,
Icarus soon collected a huge pile of feathers. Daedalus

then melted some wax and made a skeleton in the shape of a bird's wing. The smallest feathers he pressed into the soft wax and the large ones he tied on with thread. Icarus played about on the beach happily while his father worked, chasing the feathers that blew away in the strong wind that swept the island and sometimes taking bits of the wax and working it into strange shapes with his fingers.

It was fun making the wings. The sun shone on the bright feathers, the breezes ruffled them. When they were finished Daedalus fastened them to his shoulders and found himself lifted upwards, where he hung poised in the air. Filled with excitement, he made another pair for his son. They were smaller than his own, but strong and beautiful.

Finally, one clear, wind-swept morning, the wings were finished and Daedalus fastened them to Icarus's shoulders and taught him how to fly. He bade him watch the movements of the birds, how they soared and glided overhead. He pointed out the slow, graceful sweep of their wings as they beat the air steadily, without fluttering. Soon Icarus was sure that he, too, could fly and, raising his arms up and down, skimmed over the white sand and even out over the waves, letting his feet touch the snowy foam as the water thundered and broke over the sharp rocks. Daedalus watched him proudly but with misgivings. He called Icarus to his side. Putting his arm round the boy's shoulders, he said, "Icarus, my son, we are about to make our flight. No human being has ever traveled through the air before, and I want you to listen carefully to my instructions. Keep at a moderate height, for if you fly too low the fog and spray will clog your wings, and if you fly too high the heat will melt the wax that holds them together. Keep near me and you will be safe."

He kissed Icarus and fastened the wings more

securely to his son's shoulders. Icarus, standing in the
bright sun, the shining wings drooping gracefully from
his shoulders, his golden hair wet with spray and his
eyes bright and dark with excitement, looked like a
lovely bird. Daedalus's eyes filled with tears and
turning away he soared into the sky, calling to Icarus
to follow. From time to time, he looked back to see
that the boy was safe and to note how he managed his
wings in his flight. As they flew across the land to
test their prowess before setting out across the dark
wild sea, ploughmen below stopped their work and
shepherds gazed in wonder, thinking Daedalus and
Icarus were gods.

Father and son flew over Samos and Delos which lay
to their left, and Lebinthus, which lay on their right.
Icarus, beating his wings in joy, felt the thrill of the
cool wind on his face and the clear air above and below
him. He flew higher and higher up into the blue sky
until he reached the clouds. His father saw him and
called out in alarm. He tried to follow him, but he was
heavier and his wings would not carry him. Up and up
Icarus soared, through the soft moist clouds and out
again toward the glorious sun. He was bewitched by
the sense of freedom and beat his wings frantically so
that they would carry him higher and higher to heaven
itself. The blazing sun beat down on the wings and
softened the wax. Small feathers fell from the wings
and floated softly down, warning Icarus to stay his
flight and glide to earth. But the enchanted boy did
not notice them until the sun became so hot that the
largest feathers dropped off and he began to sink.
Frantically he fluttered his arms, but no feathers
remained to hold the air. He cried out to his father,
but his voice was submerged in the blue waters of the
sea, which has forever after been called by his name.

Daedalus, crazed by anxiety, called back to him,
"Icarus! Icarus, my son, where are you?" At last he

saw the feathers floating from the sky and soon his
son plunged through the clouds into the sea. Daedalus
hurried to save him, but it was too late. He gathered
the boy in his arms and flew to land, the tips of his
wings dragging in the water from the double burden
they bore. Weeping bitterly, he buried his small son
and called the land Icaria in his memory.

For more exciting myths of ancient Greece, read
Stories of the Gods and Heroes by Sally Benson, from
which these tales were taken. You'll also enjoy reading
about the adventures of Jason and other Greek heroes
in *The Golden Fleece and the Heroes Who Lived Before
Achilles* by Padraic Colum.
    Very different, but equally exciting, are the Norse
myths of ancient Scandinavia. *Legends of the North* by
Olivia Coolidge tells tales of Norse gods—the powerful
Thor, the trickster Loki, and many more.

The Highwayman
by Alfred Noyes

Part One

The wind was a torrent of darkness among the gusty trees,
The moon was a ghostly galleon tossed upon cloudy seas,
The road was a ribbon of moonlight over the purple moor,
And the highwayman came riding—
     Riding—riding—
The highwayman came riding, up to the old inn-door.

He'd a French cocked-hat on his forehead, a bunch of lace at his chin,
A coat of the claret velvet, and breeches of brown doeskin:
They fitted with never a wrinkle; his boots were up to the thigh!
And he rode with a jewelled twinkle,
        His pistol butts a-twinkle,
His rapier hilt a-twinkle, under the jewelled sky.

Over the cobbles he clattered and clashed in the dark inn-yard,
And he tapped with his whip on the shutters, but all was locked and barred:
He whistled a tune to the window, and who should be waiting there
But the landlord's black-eyed daughter,
        Bess, the landlord's daughter,
Plaiting a dark red love-knot into her long black hair.

And dark in the dark old inn-yard a stable-wicket creaked
Where Tim, the ostler, listened; his face was white and peaked,
His eyes were hollows of madness, his hair like moldy hay;
But he loved the landlord's daughter,
        The landlord's red-lipped daughter:
Dumb as a dog he listened, and he heard the robber say—

"One kiss, my bonny sweetheart, I'm after a prize tonight,
But I shall be back with the yellow gold before the morning light.
Yet if they press me sharply, and harry me through the day,
Then look for me by moonlight,
        Watch for me by moonlight:
I'll come to thee by moonlight, though Hell should bar the way."

He rose upright in the stirrups, he scarce could reach her hand;
But she loosened her hair i' the casement! His face burnt like a brand
As the black cascade of perfume came tumbling over his breast;
And he kissed its waves in the moonlight,
        (Oh, sweet black waves in the moonlight)
Then he tugged at his reins in the moonlight, and galloped away to the West.

Part Two

He did not come in the dawning; he did not come at noon;
And out of the tawny sunset, before the rise o' the moon,
When the road was a gypsy's ribbon, looping the purple moor,
A red-coat troop came marching—
      Marching—marching—
King George's men came marching, up to the old inn-door.

They said no word to the landlord, they drank his ale instead;
But they gagged his daughter and bound her to the foot of her narrow bed.
Two of them knelt at her casement, with muskets at the side!
There was death at every window;
      And Hell at one dark window;
For Bess could see, through her casement, the road that *he* would ride.

They had tied her up to attention, with many a sniggering jest:
They had bound a musket beside her, with the barrel beneath her breast!
"Now keep good watch!" and they kissed her. She heard the dead man say—
Look for me by moonlight;
      Watch for me by moonlight;
I'll come to thee by moonlight, though Hell should bar the way!

She twisted her hands behind her; but all the knots held good!
She writhed her hands till her fingers were wet with sweat or blood!
They stretched and strained in the darkness, and the hours crawled by like years;
Till, now, on the stroke of midnight,
      Cold, on the stroke of midnight,
The tip of one finger touched it! The trigger at least was hers!

The tip of one finger touched it; she strove no more for the rest!
Up, she stood up to attention, with the barrel beneath her breast,
She would not risk their hearing: she would not strive again;
For the road lay bare in the moonlight,
      Blank and bare in the moonlight;
And the blood of her veins in the moonlight throbbed to her Love's refrain.

Tlot-tlot, tlot-tlot! Had they heard it? The horse-hoofs ringing clear—
Tlot-tlot, tlot-tlot, in the distance? Were they deaf that they did not hear?
Down the ribbon of moonlight, over the brow of the hill,
The highwayman came riding,
      Riding, riding!
The red-coats looked to their priming! She stood up straight and still!

Tlot-tlot, in the frosty silence! *Tlot-tlot* in the echoing night!
Nearer he came and nearer! Her face was like a light!
Her eyes grew wide for a moment; she drew one last deep breath,
Then her finger moved in the moonlight,
     Her musket shattered the moonlight,
Shattered her breast in the moonlight and warned him—with her death.

He turned; he spurred to the West; he did not know who stood
Bowed with her head o'er the musket, drenched with her own red blood!
Not till the dawn he heard it, and his face grew gray to hear
How Bess, the landlord's daughter,
     The landlord's black-eyed daughter,
Had watched for her Love in the moonlight; and died in the darkness there.

Back he spurred like a madman, shrieking a curse to the sky,
With the white road smoking behind him, and his rapier brandished high!
Blood-red were his spurs in the golden noon; wine-red was his velvet coat;
When they shot him down on the highway,
     Down like a dog on the highway,
And he lay in his blood on the highway, with the bunch of lace at his throat.

. . . .

And still of a winter's night, they say, when the wind is in the trees,
When the moon is a ghostly galleon tossed upon cloudy seas,
When the road is a ribbon of moonlight over the purple moor,
A highwayman comes riding—
　　　Riding—riding—
A highwayman comes riding, up to the old inn-door.

Over the cobbles he clatters and clangs in the dark inn-yard;
And he taps with his whip on the shutters, but all is locked and barred:
He whistles a tune to the window, and who should be waiting there
But the landlord's black-eyed daughter,
　　　Bess, the landlord's daughter,
Plaiting a dark red love-knot into her long black hair.

The Storm

from *Hills End*
by Ivan Southall

Elaine Godwin, a schoolteacher in a small Australian
town, has a great interest in the rocks, plants, and
creatures of the surrounding mountains. When Adrian,
one of her students, tells of finding a cave with
paintings that must have been done by Aborigines a
long time ago, she is very excited. But most of
Adrian's friends think he has just told another of his
whoppers to get out of trouble. Together, they set off
into the mountains to find the cave.

⚜ ⚜ ⚜

At the foot of the bluff Miss Godwin gathered her
children round her. She was guilty of deceiving them.
They thought she only wanted to talk but really she
wanted to rest. She felt like a jelly inside, quivery and
without any strength. She knew now that this climb up
the bluff was every bit as bad as she had feared. This
was why she hadn't climbed it when she had come
before; it had been simply common sense, not
cowardice.

She drew her book from her haversack and it fell
open at a photograph of the rock paintings at
Lightning Totem Centre in North Australia.

"... Now take a good look at these, Adrian, and tell
me if you find any similarities to what you saw."

Adrian had been through this before. "No," he said.

"You're sure?"

"Certain, miss."

"I'm going to ask you once more, Adrian, to go through the book from cover to cover and make your selection. There must be similarities somewhere."

"I told you about the red hands, miss."

"That doesn't help much, Adrian. There are thousands of red hands throughout the continent. It is their association with these other things that is mystifying."

Paul sighed inwardly. Of course the association was mystifying. It wasn't even true. But Miss Godwin had spoken about this, over and over again. She was excited by it. She had kept harping on it, perhaps trying to break Adrian's story down, but Adrian's story had never broken. He hadn't changed a detail. He had described things which, Miss Godwin said, had never been found before. They must have been made a very long time ago, perhaps thousands of years ago, by artists out of touch with all other men.

So she waited while Adrian thumbed over the book again, from photograph to photograph, endeavoring to steady her nerves and marshal her strength. If she failed to make the climb what would these children think of a teacher who taught them to explore but was afraid to explore herself? What would they think of a teacher who enthused about the art of the Stone Age men but was too frightened to make a personal effort to see it?

"Really, miss," said Adrian, closing the book and passing it back to her, "it might be that I've forgotten, but I'm sure they were different."

"Very well, Adrian." Miss Godwin glanced at her watch. "We'll find out how good an explorer you are. I think you'd better lead the way with Paul, don't you, and the rest of us can follow very carefully?"

"Yes, miss. There's no danger really. It looks much worse than it is. There's only one thing. Don't look down unless you've got something to hang on to."

"Do you hear that, children? Adrian says there's no danger and Adrian knows. But if any of you would rather stay down here just say the word."

Gussie would have liked to have stayed, very, very much, but she was frightened that everyone would tease her. She didn't like the look of the water trickling from the rocks, or the moss and the slime. And her legs were aching, with the awful ache that she got sometimes and that her mother called "growing pains." It didn't seem right that it hurt to grow, Gussie thought, but perhaps that was why the trees groaned sometimes. Perhaps it hurt them, too.

Maisie, too, was rather anxious, but she was frightened to speak up, frightened that everyone would make fun of her.

"If it is an important discovery," she said, "will we all be famous?"

"I don't know about that," said Miss Godwin. "Adrian will be the famous one. We'll have to name the discovery after him."

"Golly!" said Paul, shaken for the moment. "Can we do that?"

"Of course we can. It's our right, and if the Government agrees the caves will be known by his name for ever and ever."

"No kiddin'?" queried Adrian.

Miss Godwin coughed discreetly. "That isn't quite the word, Adrian, but it is a fact. They'll be named in your honor." Perhaps she was rueful then. She wasn't selfish, but it would have been nice if they had suggested the discovery be named after her. She couldn't expect children to think of that.

"Come along, then. Let's start."

The heat was very trying and Miss Elaine Godwin shuffled up the face of the bluff, perspiring freely, shaking so much at the knees that she was sure they

were knocking together. Dear, dear, dear! Why couldn't she act her age and admit it was too much for her? She was groaning for breath and her pulse was beating so hard in her temples that all she could hear was its thud-thud-thud. And, bless her soul, she'd have to get down again afterward. That would be worse by far. It was this continual patter of little stones, and the times she slipped on wet rocks or slime, the times she looked down because the depths drew her eyes with a dreadful fascination, the times she groped for a foothold and sent a shower of fragments on the children beneath her. The times she was giddy and her head swam, the times she wanted to scream at the top of her voice, yet had to say so calmly, "Come along, children."

Suddenly she was there, on the wide ledge that formed the opening to a cave, and Paul was smiling at her and Adrian seemed unusually subdued.

"Well, well, well," she said breathlessly. "Here we are."

Harvey, Gussie, Maisie, and finally Frances came up on the ledge behind her. The girls were flushed and excited, full of their achievement because not too many girls had got as far as this before. They had been surprised to discover that the way up was far less dangerous than they had been told. Of course, they had had to be careful, but no more careful than in climbing a tree.

Miss Godwin was still fluttery and was finding it difficult to conceal her distress. All she wanted to do was sit down, and she never knew how she resisted the yearning. She was a brave soul and a far better leader than she gave herself credit for. They never dreamed that she was frightened, never imagined the state of her mind.

"Now, Adrian," she said, "we're in your hands."

"Have you brought a torch, Miss Godwin?"

"Of course. Of course. Always prepared."

Miss Godwin's torch was an electric lantern, six volts, and its power would last for days.

"Is it very far in, Adrian?"

"No miss. So long as we find the right cave it's only a few yards."

"Goodness!" Miss Godwin was rather stern. "You have no doubt that you can find it?"

"Oh, no. It might take a little time, but I'll find it."

"Very well. As I said, we're in your hands. Take the torch. We don't know how soon we'll need it. The sunlight won't last for ever."

It was Gussie who was left behind. She was so enthralled by the great rock bed lying beneath her that these silly caves pitting the face of the bluff seemed unimportant. She had climbed high, right up here, and the view was the reward, the depth of space, the impression that she was sitting in an airplane looking over the side. She simply didn't notice the sky until suddenly there were no shadows.

She glanced up and the sun had vanished behind the strangest looking cloud she had ever seen. It seemed to have reached out of the north like a big black arm and closed its hand round the sun.

"Ooh," she said. "Look at that."

She turned, and there was no one to look. They'd all gone.

"Oh, brother!" she said. "Wait for me. *Wait for me!*"

"Goodness!" exclaimed Miss Elaine Godwin. "What was that?"

She knew what it was, really, but she was so accustomed to putting questions to children that she felt obliged to ask.

"That was thunder," said Frances.

"Thunder, indeed. I hope we're all not going to get wet on the way home."

She wasn't thinking that at all. Her only thought was her fear of descending the bluff. If rain came with the thunder the footholds would be like glass, and somehow she was sure it was raining; although these caves were warm there was in the air the touch and smell of water or ice.

"Children," she said, "I think we'd better go back to the entrance to see what's happening."

"I'll go, miss," said Paul. "I know my way. I'll only be half a minute."

"Thank you all the same, Paul, but we must keep

together. We have only the one torch, and I don't wish to be left in the dark, nor do I wish you to be stumbling alone in the dark. Lead the way, Adrian."

"Fancy a storm on a day like this!" said Gussie. "Ooh!"

"Yes, Augusta?" said Miss Godwin. "What did you mean by that tone of surprise?"

"I must have seen it coming. I saw a cloud. The funniest cloud you ever saw."

Miss Godwin shivered. "What was funny about it, Augusta?"

"It was like a big black arm, reaching across the sky, taking hold of the sun."

"You should have told me, child." Her voice was so sharp that they were surprised. "Hurry on, Adrian. If there's to be a storm we must get out of here."

They followed the beam of the torch, this way and that way, but Miss Godwin was bustling so busily on Adrian's heels that she confused him and he took the wrong turning. He wasn't certain in his mind that he was wrong, but the doubt was there, and Paul said, "Not this way, Adrian."

"We'll leave that to Adrian, shall we?" snapped Miss Godwin.

"But he might be right, miss," stammered Adrian. "I—I think he is right."

"Nonsense. I distinctly remember this chamber. Hurry on."

But Adrian knew he didn't remember it, not from any of his journeys in here, and when the pale whiteness of old bones moved into the beam of the torch he was certain he'd never set foot in this cave before.

He heard the sharp intake of Miss Godwin's breath close to his ear, heard the squeal from Harvey and the gasp from Paul.

"Wait!"

Miss Godwin took the torch from Adrian and directed it across the floor of the cave to a ledge. There were many bones, huge bones, and kangaroo skulls twice as large as any they had ever seen, and on the walls beyond were red hands and black hands and white hands and drawings of animals and devil men.

Miss Godwin sighed, a deep, shuddering sigh, and Gussie cried out, and Paul was so ashamed he wished the ground would open up and swallow him.

Adrian was panting in wonderment, in amazement, in absolute elation. They were here. The drawings *were* here. And they'd called him a liar. That prim and proper Paul had called him a liar and he wasn't a liar at all.

"I'm sorry, Adrian," Paul murmured. "Golly, I am sorry!"

Frances, strangely, was a little saddened. She had believed Adrian yet she was sorry that Paul had been proved wrong—and Gussie was all confused. She had been so sure that Adrian had been lying. So very, very sure, because Paul had been so sure.

Suddenly all were talking at once, and Miss Godwin had to raise her voice to a shout. "Be quiet!"

She waited a few moments. "That's better. That's very much better. Now, no one is to touch a single thing. Before we make any examination I want to photograph everything just as we find it. . . . Adrian, this is a most wonderful, wonderful discovery. My only regret is that I didn't come a week ago. Imagine it, children—Hills End will be famous. We'll have anthropologists coming here. Great scholars from all over the world. Children, children, this is the most wonderful thing that has ever happened to us. Oh dear, I—I'm really so excited. I'm all of a flutter. Adrian, my boy." She thrust her arm round him and hugged him tight. "Why didn't you tell us about the bones, too? Didn't you think they were important? They're the bones of the giant kangaroo—and the diprotodon, I think. Adrian, Adrian, these animals have been extinct for tens of thousands—perhaps hundreds of thousands—of years. . . . Goodness me, I'm all of a flutter! I—I cannot believe my eyes. I'm going to wake up in a minute. Oh dear, dear, dear!"

"You won't wake up, Miss Godwin," said Paul. "It's real. Really and truly real."

She sighed again, a shivering and breathless sigh. "Take the torch, Paul. Shine it on my haversack. I—I must get my things."

She was trembling so much she could hardly undo the straps and she took out her camera and her tripod and her flashlight fittings, and suddenly heard the thunderclaps again and felt the cold air that was rapidly expelling the warmth from the caves.

She looked up with a troubled frown and slowly stood erect, leaving her precious equipment at her feet. "First of all," she said, "I think we'd better take a look at the weather. We mustn't lose our sense of proportion. These drawings will be here tomorrow—next week—they'll remain. We must take a look at the weather."

"*Now*, miss?"

"Certainly, Adrian. But we must make sure that we don't lose our cave. It took a long while to find it, even though you were sure you knew where it was. Now, what shall we do?"

"I'll go, miss" said Paul. "I said before it would be all right."

"No. We stay together. While you're with me you're my responsibility. There had been no warning of a storm. This was some trick of the weather. Some local disturbance. . . . "Now what shall we do? Of course, what we want is a ball of string. That's it. A ball of string. Always be prepared, children. That's the division between the foolish and the wise."

She took the ball of string from her haversack, tied the loose end round a heavy stone, and directed Paul to proceed in front with the torch while she paid out the string behind her.

So they came again toward the opening, toward a world of frightening sound and vivid lightning flashes, of bitter cold, of violent wind, of torrential rain and hailstones. The hailstones struck the ledge and bounced and were as big as golf balls. They couldn't approach the opening. They had to stop well back, clear of showering ice and wind-driven rain. The world beyond was like a block of frosted glass—water, ice, and wind in a mass through which they could not see.

The tremendous storm that sweeps over the mountains creates havoc. The children, separated from their teacher, manage to get back to the town of Hills End only to find it flooded and deserted. They are on their own in a struggle to survive. Ivan Southall, the author of *Hills End,* is one of Australia's best writers of children's books. Another of his stories you might like is *Ash Road,* which is about a group of children caught in the path of a devastating fire.

Wild Geese
by Elinor Chipp

I heard the wild geese flying
   In the dead of the night,
With beat of wings and crying
   I heard the wild geese flying,
And dreams in my heart sighing
   Followed their northward flight.
I heard the wild geese flying
   In the dead of the night.

A Vagabond Song
by Bliss Carman

There is something in the autumn that is native to my blood—
Touch of manner, hint of mood;
And my heart is like a rhyme,
With the yellow and the purple and the crimson keeping time.

The scarlet of the maples can shake me like a cry
Of bugles going by.
And my lonely spirit thrills
To see the frosty asters like smoke upon the hills.

There is something in October sets the gypsy blood astir;
We must rise and follow her,
When from every hill of flame
She calls and calls each vagabond by name.

230

The Sea Gypsy
by Richard Hovey

I am fevered with the sunset,
I am fretful with the bay,
For the wander-thirst is on me
And my soul is in Cathay.

There's a schooner in the offing,
With her top-sails shot with fire,
And my heart has gone aboard her
For the Islands of Desire.

I must forth again tomorrow!
With the sunset I must be,
Hull down on the trail of rapture
In the wonder of the Sea.

Home Thoughts from Abroad
by Robert Browning

Oh, to be in England
Now that April's there,
And whoever wakes in England
Sees, some morning, unaware,
That the lowest boughs and the brush-wood sheaf
Round the elm-tree bole are in tiny leaf,
While the chaffinch sings on the orchard bough
In England—now!

A Stranger in the Land

from *The Witch of Blackbird Pond*
by Elizabeth George Speare

All her life, Kit Tyler has lived with her wealthy
grandfather on the warm, sunny island of Barbados in
the West Indies. When her grandfather dies, the only
family left is an aunt in Wethersfield, Connecticut.
Hoping to live with her aunt, sixteen-year-old Kit
takes passage on a ship bound for Connecticut. For
days now, the *Dolphin* has been working its way
slowly up the Connecticut River toward Wethersfield.
It is the year 1687, and to Kit the land seems as bleak
and forbidding as the people she has met.

⚜ ⚜ ⚜

Early the next morning a contrary breeze came
whistling along the river. The *Dolphin* sprang to life,
scudded the last few miles, and bumped against the
wharf at Wethersfield landing. The shore, muffled in
thick scarves of drifting mist, looked scarcely different
from the miles of unbroken forest that they had seen
for the past week.

Sailors began vigorously to roll out the great casks
of molasses and pile them along the wharf. Two of the
men lowered over the side the seven small leather
trunks that held all of Kit's belongings and piled them,
one beside the other, on the wet planking. Kit
clambered down the ladder and stood for the second
time on the alien shore that was to be her home.

Her heart sank. This was Wethersfield! Just a

narrow sandy stretch of shoreline, a few piles sunk in
the river with rough planking for a platform. Out of
the mist jutted a row of cavernous wooden structures
that must be warehouses, and beyond that the dense,
dripping green of fields and woods. No town, not a
house, only a few men and boys and two yapping dogs
who had come to meet the boat. With something like
panic Kit watched Goodwife Cruff descend the ladder
and stride ahead of her husband along the wharf.
Prudence, dragging at her mother's hand, gazed back
imploringly as they passed.

"Ma," she ventured timidly, "the pretty lady got off
here at Wethersfield!"

Kit summoned the boldness to speak to her. "Yes,

Prudence," she called clearly. "And I hope that I will see you often."

Goodwife Cruff halted and glared at Kit. "I'll thank you to let my child alone!" she spat out. "We do not welcome strangers in this town, and you be the kind we like least." Jerking Prudence nearly off her feet, she marched firmly up the dirt road and disappeared in the fog.

Even John Holbrook's farewells were abstracted. A formal bow, a polite wish for her pleasant arrival, and he, too, strode eagerly into the fog in quest of his new teacher. Then Kit saw Captain Eaton approaching and knew that the moment had come when the truth would have to be told.

"There must be some mistake," the captain began. "We signaled yesterday that we would reach Wethersfield at dawn. I expected that your aunt and uncle would be here to meet you no matter how early it might be."

Kit swallowed and gathered her courage. "Captain Eaton," she said boldly, "my uncle and aunt can hardly be blamed for not meeting me. You see—well, to be honest, they do not even know that I am coming."

The captain's jaw tightened. "You gave me to understand that they had sent for you to come."

Kit lifted her head proudly. "I told you that they wanted me," she corrected him. "Mistress Wood is my mother's sister. Naturally she would always want me to come."

"Even assuming that to be true, how could you be sure they were still in Connecticut?"

"My Aunt Rachel's last letter came only six months ago."

He scowled with annoyance. "You know very well that I should never have taken you on board had I known this. Now I shall have to take the time to find where your uncle lives and deliver you. But understand, I take no responsibility for your coming."

Kit's head went higher. "I am entirely responsible for my own coming," she assured him haughtily.

"Fair enough," the captain responded grimly. "Look here, Nat," he turned back. "See if two hands can be spared to carry this baggage."

Kit's cheeks went scarlet. Why should Nat, who had carefully been somewhere else during the whole of the last nine days, have to be so handy at just this moment? Now whatever befell he was going to be there to witness it, with those mocking blue eyes and that maddening cool amusement. What if Aunt Rachel—but there was no time for doubt now. Between trying to hold up her head confidently and at the same time find a place to set down her dainty kid shoes between the slimy ruts and the mud puddles, Kit had all she could tend to.

Along with her pretty shoes, Kit's spirits sank lower at each step. She had clutched at a hope that the dark fringe of dripping trees might somehow be concealing the town she had anticipated. But as they plodded along the dirt road past wide stumpy fields, her last hopes died. There was no fine town of Wethersfield. There was a mere settlement, far more lonely and dreary than Saybrook.

A man in a leather coat and breeches led a cow along the road. He stopped to stare at them, and even the cow looked astonished. Captain Eaton took advantage of the meeting to ask directions.

"High Street," the man said, pointing his jagged stick. "Matthew Wood's place is the third house beyond the Common."

High Street indeed! No more than a cow path! Kit's shoes were wet through, and the soaked ruffles of her gown slapped against her ankles. She would naturally have lifted her skirts free of the uncut grass, but a new self-consciousness restrained her. She was aware at every step of the young man who strode behind her with a trunk balanced easily on each shoulder.

She relaxed slightly at the first glimpse of her uncle's house. At least it looked solid and respectable, compared to the cabins they had passed. Two and a half stories it stood, gracefully proportioned, with leaded glass windows and clapboards weathered to a silvery gray.

The captain lifted the iron knocker and let it fall with a thud that echoed in the pit of the girl's stomach. For a moment she could not breathe at all. Then the door opened and a thin, gray-haired woman stood on the threshold. She was quite plainly a servant, and Kit was impatient when the captain removed his hat and spoke with courtesy.

"Do I have the honor of addressing—?"

The woman did not even hear him. Her look had flashed past to the girl who stood just behind, and her face had suddenly gone white. One hand reached to clutch the doorpost.

"Margaret!" The word was no more than a whisper. For a moment the two women stared at each other. Then realization swept over Kit.

"No, Aunt Rachel!" she cried. "Don't look like that! It is Kit! I am Margaret's daughter."

"Kit? You mean—can it possibly be Katherine Tyler? For a moment I thought—oh, my dear child, how wonderful!"

All at once such a warmth and happiness swept over her pale face that Kit too was startled. Yes, this strange woman was indeed Aunt Rachel, and once, a long time ago, she must have been very beautiful.

Captain Eaton cleared his throat. "Well," he observed, "I am relieved that this has turned out well after all. What will you have me do with the baggage, ma'am?"

Rachel Wood's eyes focused for the first time on the three trunk bearers. "Goodness," she gasped, "do all these belong to you, child? You can just set them there,

I suppose, and I'll ask my husband about them. Can I
offer you and your men some breakfast, sir?"

"Thank you, we can't spare any more time. Good
day, young lady. I'll tell my wife I saw you safely
here."

"I'm sorry to have caused you trouble," Kit said
sincerely. "And I do thank you, all of you."

Two of the three sailors had already started back
along the road, but Nat still stood beside the trunks
and looked down at her. As their eyes met, something
flashed between them, a question that was suddenly

weighted with regret. But the instant was gone before she could grasp it, and the mocking light has sprung again into his eyes.

"Remember," he said softly. "Only the guilty ones stay afloat."[1] And then he was gone.

The doorway of Matthew Wood's house led into a shallow hallway from which a narrow flight of stairs climbed steeply. Through a second door Kit stepped into the welcome of the great kitchen. In a fireplace that filled half one side of the room a bright fire crackled, throwing glancing patterns of light on creamy plaster walls. There was a gleam of rubbed wood and burnished pewter.

"Matthew! Girls!" cried her aunt. "Something wonderful has happened! Here is Katherine Tyler, my sister Margaret's girl, come all the way from Barbados!"

Three people stared up at her from the plain board table. Then, from his place at the head, a man unfolded his tall angular body and came toward her.

"You are welcome, Katherine," he said gravely, and took her hand in his bony fingers. She could not read the faintest sign of welcome in his thin stern lips or in the dark eyes that glowered fiercely at her from under heavy grizzled eyebrows.

Behind him a girl sprang up from the table and came forward. "This is your cousin Judith," her aunt said, and Kit gasped with pleasure. Judith's face fulfilled in every exquisite detail the picture she had treasured of her imagined aunt. The clear white skin, the blue eyes under the dark fringe of lashes, the black hair that curled against her shoulders, and the haughty lift of her perfect small chin—this girl could have been the toast of a regiment!

---

1. Nat is referring to the trial by water as a way of finding out if a woman is a witch. The suspected woman was tied hand and foot and thrown into deep water. If she floated, she was guilty. If she sank she was innocent.

"And your other cousin, Mercy." The second girl had
risen more slowly, and at first Kit was only aware of
the most extraordinary eyes she had ever seen, gray as
rain at sea, wide and clear and filled with light. Then,
as Mercy stepped forward, one shoulder dipped and
jerked back grotesquely, and Kit realized that she
leaned on crutches.

"How lovely," breathed Mercy, her voice as arresting
as her eyes, "to see you after all these years,
Katherine!"

"Will you call me Kit?" The question sounded abrupt.
Kit had been her grandfather's name for her, and
something in Mercy's smile had reached straight across

the gulf so that suddenly she wanted to hear the name spoken again.

"Have you had breakfast?"

"I guess not. I hadn't even thought of it."

"Then 'tis lucky we are eating late this morning," said her aunt. "Take her cloak, Judith. Come close to the fire, my dear, your skirt is soaking."

As Kit threw back the woolen cloak, Judith's reaching hand fell back. "My goodness!" she exclaimed. "You wore a dress like that to *travel* in?"

In her eagerness to make a good impression Kit had selected this dress with care, but here in this plain room it seemed overelegant. The three other women were all wearing some nondescript sort of coarse gray stuff. Judith laid the cloak thoughtfully on a bench and reached to touch Kit's glove.

"What beautiful embroidery," she said admiringly.

"Do you like them? I'll give you some just like them if you like. I have several pairs in my trunk."

Judith's eyes narrowed. Rachel Wood was setting out a pewter mug and spoon and a crude wooden plate.

"Sit here, Katherine, where the fire will warm your back. Tell us how you happened to come so far. Did your grandfather come with you?"

"My grandfather died four months ago," Kit explained.

"Why, you poor child! All alone there on that island! Who did come with you, then?"

"I came alone."

"Praise be!" her aunt marveled. "Well, you're here safe and sound. Have some corn bread, my dear. 'Twas baked fresh yesterday, and there is new butter."

Surprisingly, the bread tasted delicious, though of a coarse texture like nothing she had ever tasted before. Kit lifted the pewter mug thirstily, and abruptly set it down. "Is that *water?*" she asked politely.

"Of course, drawn fresh from the spring this morning."

Water! For *breakfast!* But the corn bread was good, and she managed a second piece in spite of her dry tongue.

Rachel Wood could not seem to look away from the young face across the table, and every few moments her eyes brimmed over with tears.

"I declare, you look so like her it takes my breath away. But all the same, there is a hint of your father there, too. I can see it if I look closely."

"You remember my father?" Kit asked eagerly.

"I remember him well. A fine upstanding lad he was, and I never could blame Margaret. But it broke my heart to have her go so far."

But Rachel had come even farther. What could she have seen in that fierce silent man to draw her away from England? Could he have been handsome? Perhaps, with that strong regal nose and high forehead. But so terrifying!

Matthew Wood had not sat down at the table with the others. Though he had said nothing, Kit had been aware that not a motion had escaped his intent scowl. Now he pulled down a leather jacket from a peg on the wall and thrust his long arms into the sleeves.

"I will be working in the south meadow," he told his wife. "You had best not expect me till sundown."

At the open door, however, he stopped and looked back at them. "What is all this?" he inquired coldly.

"Oh," said Kit, scrambling to her feet. "I forgot. Those are my trunks."

"Yours? Seven trunks? What can be in them?"

"Why—my clothes, and a few things of Grandfather's."

"Seven trunks of clothes, all the way from Barbados just for a visit?"

The cold measured word fell like so many stones into the quiet room. Kit's throat was so dry she longed now to swallow the water. She lifted her chin and looked directly into those searching eyes.

"I have not come for a visit, sir." she answered. "I have come to stay with you."

There was a little gasp from Rachel. Matthew Wood closed the door deliberately and came back toward the table. "Why did you not write to us first?"

All her life, whenever her grandfather had asked her a question he had expected a direct answer. Now, in this stern man facing her, so totally different from her grandfather, Kit sensed the same quality of directness, and out of an instinctive respect she gave the only honest answer she could.

"I did not dare to write," she said. "I was afraid that you might not tell me to come, and I had to come."

Rachel leaned forward to put a hand on Kit's arm.

"We would not have refused you if you were in need," said her uncle. "But a step like this should not be taken without due pondering."

"Matthew," protested Rachel timidly, "what is there to ponder? We are the only family she has. Let us talk about it later. Now Katherine is tired, and your work has been delayed already."

Matthew Wood drew up a chair and sat down heavily. "The work will have to wait," he said. "It is best that we understand this matter at once. How did you come to set sail all alone?"

"There was a ship in the harbor and they said it was from Connecticut. I should have sent a letter, I know, but it might have been months before another ship came. So instead of writing I decided to come myself."

"You mean that, just on an impulse, you left your rightful home and sailed halfway across the world?"

"No, it was not an impulse exactly. You see, I really had no home to leave."

"What of your grandfather's estate? I always understood he was a wealthy man."

"I suppose he was wealthy, once. But he had not been well for a long time. I think for years he was not able to manage the plantation, but no one realized it. He left everything more and more to the overseer, a man named Bryant. Last winter Bryant sold off the whole crop and then disappeared. Probably he sailed back to England on the trading ship. Grandfather couldn't believe it. After that he was never really well. The other plantation owners were his friends. Nobody ever pressed him, but after he died there just seemed to be debts everywhere, wherever I turned."

"Did you pay them?"

"Yes, every one of them. All the land had to be sold, and the house and the slaves, and all the furniture from England. There wasn't anything left, not even enough for my passage. To pay my way on the ship I had to sell my own Negro girl."

"Humph!" With one syllable Matthew disposed of the sacrifice, only a little less sharp than Grandfather's loss, of the little African slave who had been her shadow for twelve years. There was an awkward silence. Kit found Mercy's eyes and was steadied by the quiet sympathy she saw there. Then her aunt came to put an arm across her shoulder.

"Poor Katherine! It must have been terrible for you! You were perfectly right to come to us. You do believe she was right, don't you Matthew?"

"Yes," her husband conceded harshly. "She was right, I suppose, since we are her only kin. I will bring in the baggage." At the door he turned again. "Your grandfather was a King's man, I reckon?"

"He was a Royalist, sir. Here in America are you not also subjects of King James?"

Without answering, Matthew Wood left the room. Seven times he returned, bending his tall frame to enter the doorway, and with wordless disapproval set down one after the other the seven small trunks. They filled one entire end of the room.

"Where on earth can we put them?" quavered her aunt. "I will find a place for them later in the attic," said her husband. "Seven trunks! The whole town will be talking about it before nightfall."

If you enjoyed this part of The Witch of Blackbird Pond, *you will want to read the rest of the book. As you might expect, high-spirited Kit rebels against many of the Puritan ways of life, especially the persecution of so-called witches. And this leads to Kit herself being accused of witchcraft and brought to trial. You might also try another of Mrs. Speare's books,* Calico Captive, *an exciting tale, based on actual events, of a girl captured by Indians.*

Fog

by Carl Sandburg

The fog comes
on little cat feet.

It sits looking
over harbor and city
on silent haunches
and then moves on.

Swift Things
Are Beautiful

by Elizabeth Coatsworth

Swift things are beautiful:
Swallows and deer,
And lightning that falls
Bright-veined and clear,
Rivers and meteors,
Wind in the wheat,
The strong-withered horse,
The runner's sure feet.

And slow things are beautiful:
The closing of day,
The pause of the wave
That curves downward to spray,
The ember that crumbles,
The opening flower
And the ox that moves on
In the quiet of power.

Wanted—A Witch's Cat

by Shelagh McGee

Wanted—a witch's cat.
Must have vigor and spite,
Be expert at hissing,
And good in a fight,
And have balance and poise
On a broomstick at night.

Wanted—a witch's cat.
Must have hypnotic eyes
To tantalize victims
And mesmerize spies,
And be an adept
At scanning the skies.

Wanted—a witch's cat,
With a sly, cunning smile,
A knowledge of spells
And a good deal of guile,
With a fairly hot temper
And plenty of bile.

Wanted—a witch's cat,
Who's not afraid to fly,
For a cat with strong nerves
The salary's high
Wanted—a witch's cat;
Only the best need apply.

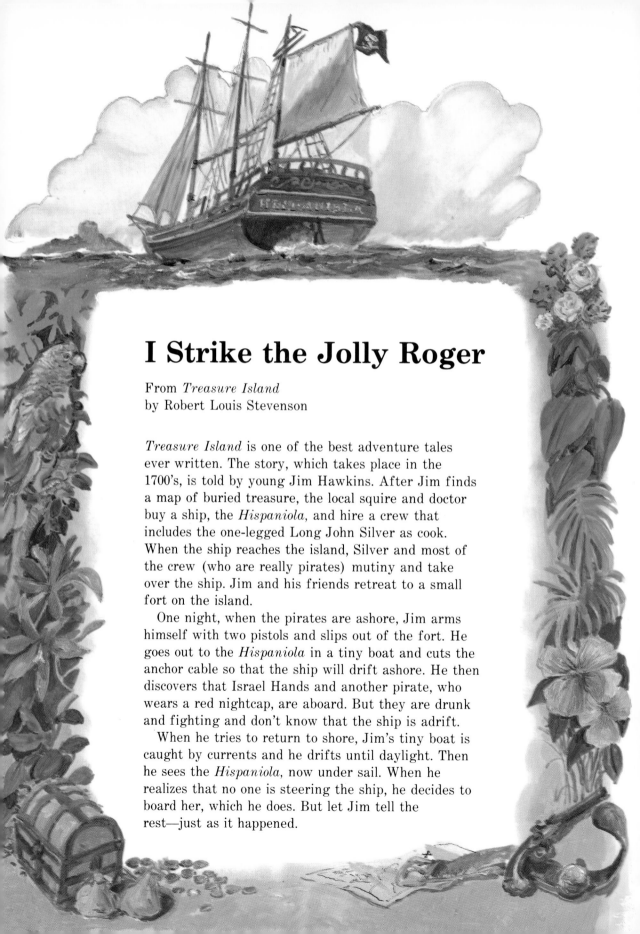

I Strike the Jolly Roger

From *Treasure Island*
by Robert Louis Stevenson

Treasure Island is one of the best adventure tales
ever written. The story, which takes place in the
1700's, is told by young Jim Hawkins. After Jim finds
a map of buried treasure, the local squire and doctor
buy a ship, the *Hispaniola*, and hire a crew that
includes the one-legged Long John Silver as cook.
When the ship reaches the island, Silver and most of
the crew (who are really pirates) mutiny and take
over the ship. Jim and his friends retreat to a small
fort on the island.

One night, when the pirates are ashore, Jim arms
himself with two pistols and slips out of the fort. He
goes out to the *Hispaniola* in a tiny boat and cuts the
anchor cable so that the ship will drift ashore. He then
discovers that Israel Hands and another pirate, who
wears a red nightcap, are aboard. But they are drunk
and fighting and don't know that the ship is adrift.

When he tries to return to shore, Jim's tiny boat is
caught by currents and he drifts until daylight. Then
he sees the *Hispaniola*, now under sail. When he
realizes that no one is steering the ship, he decides to
board her, which he does. But let Jim tell the
rest—just as it happened.

There were the two watchmen, sure enough: red-cap on his back, as stiff as a handspike, with his arms stretched out like those of a crucifix, and his teeth showing through his open lips; Israel Hands propped against the bulwarks, his chin on his chest, his hands lying open before him on the deck, his face as white, under its tan, as a tallow candle.

At every jump of the schooner, red-cap slipped to and fro; but—what was ghastly to behold—neither his attitude nor his fixed teeth-disclosing grin was anyway disturbed by this rough usage. At every jump, too, Hands appeared still more to sink into himself and settle down upon the deck, his feet sliding ever the farther out, and the whole body canting towards the stern, so that his face became, little by little, hid from me; and at last I could see nothing beyond his ear and the frayed ringlet of one whisker.

At the same time, I observed, around both of them, splashes of dark blood upon the planks, and began to feel sure that they had killed each other in their drunken wrath.

While I was thus looking and wondering, in a calm moment, when the ship was still, Israel Hands turned partly round, and, with a low moan, writhed himself back to the position in which I had seen him first.

I walked aft until I reached the main-mast.

"Come aboard, Mr. Hands," I said, ironically.

He rolled his eyes round heavily; but he was too far gone to express surprise. All he could do was to utter one word, "Brandy."

It occurred to me there was no time to lose; and, dodging the boom as it once more lurched across the deck, I slipped aft, and down the companion stairs into the cabin.

It was such a scene of confusion as you can hardly fancy. All the lockfast places had been broken open in quest of the chart. The floor was thick with mud, where ruffians had sat down to drink or consult after wading in the marshes round their camp. The bulkheads, all painted in clear white, and beaded round with gilt, bore a pattern of dirty hands. Dozens of empty bottles clinked together in corners to the rolling of the ship. One of the doctor's medical books lay open on the table, half of the leaves gutted out, I suppose, for pipelights. In the midst of all this the lamp still cast a smoky glow, obscure and brown as umber.

I went into the cellar; all the barrels were gone, and of the bottles a most surprising number had been drunk out and thrown away. Certainly, since the mutiny began, not a man of them could ever have been sober.

Foraging about, I found a bottle with some brandy left, for Hands; and for myself I routed out some biscuit, some pickled fruits, a great bunch of raisins, and a piece of cheese. With these I came on deck, put down my own stock behind the rudder head, and well out of the coxswain's[1] reach, went forward to the water-breaker, and had a good, deep drink of water, and then, and not till then, gave Hands the brandy.

He must have drunk a gill before he took the bottle from his mouth.

"Aye," said he, "by thunder, but I wanted some o' that!"

I had sat down already in my own corner and begun to eat.

"Much hurt?" I asked him.

He grunted, or, rather, I might say, he barked.

"If that doctor was aboard," he said, "I'd be right enough in a couple of turns; but I don't have no manner of luck, you see, and that's what's the matter with me. As for that swab, he's good and dead, he is," he added, indicating the man with the red cap. "He

---

1. A coxswain (KAHK suhn) is a sailor who has charge of a small boat and its crew and usually steers.

warn't no seaman, anyhow. And where mought you
have come from?"

"Well," said I, "I've come aboard to take possession
of this ship, Mr. Hands; and you'll please regard me as
your captain until further notice."

He looked at me sourly enough, but said nothing.
Some of the colour had come back into his cheeks,
though he still looked very sick, and still continued to
slip out and settle down as the ship banged about.

"By-the-by," I continued, "I can't have these colours,
Mr. Hands; and, by your leave, I'll strike 'em.[2] Better
none than these."

And, again dodging the boom, I ran to the colour
lines, handed down their cursed black flag, and
chucked it overboard.

"God save the king!" said I, waving my cap; "and
there's an end to Captain Silver!"

---

2. To strike the colours means to lower the flag. The flag in this case
is the Jolly Roger—the pirates' black flag with a white skull and
crossbones on it.

He watched me keenly and slyly, his chin all the while on his breast.

"I reckon," he said at last—"I reckon, Cap'n Hawkins, you'll kind of want to get ashore, now. S'pose we talks."

"Why, yes," says I, "with all my heart, Mr. Hands. Say on." And I went back to my meal with a good appetite.

"This man," he began, nodding feebly at the corpse—"O'Brien were his name—a rank Irelander—this man and me got the canvas on her, meaning for to sail her back. Well, *he's* dead now, he is—as dead as bilge; and who's to sail this ship, I don't see. Without I gives you a hint, you ain't that man, as far's I can tell. Now, look here, you gives me food and drink, and a old scarf or ankecher to tie my wound up, you do; and I'll tell you how to sail her; and that's about square all round, I take it."

"I'll tell you one thing," says I: "I'm not going back to Captain Kidd's anchorage.[3] I mean to get into North Inlet, and beach her quietly there."

"To be sure you did," he cried. "Why, I ain't sich an infernal lubber, after all. I can see, can't I? I've tried my fling, I have, and I've lost, and it's you has the wind of me. North Inlet? Why, I haven't no ch'ice, not I! I'd help you sail her up to Execution Dock,[4] by thunder! so I would."

Well, as it seemed to me, there was some sense in this. We struck our bargain on the spot. In three minutes I had the *Hispaniola* sailing easily before the wind along the coast of Treasure Island, with good hopes of turning the northern point ere noon, and

---

3. Captain Kidd's anchorage was at the southeastern end of the island. It was named for William Kidd, a famous pirate who was hung in 1701.
4. Execution Dock is the place in London where Captain Kidd and other pirates were hanged in chains at low water and left for three tides.

beating down again as far as North Inlet before high water, when we might beach her safely, and wait till the subsiding tide permitted us to land.

Then I lashed the tiller and went below to my own chest, where I got a soft silk handkerchief of my mother's. With this, and with my aid, Hands bound up the great bleeding stab he had received in the thigh, and after he had eaten a little and had a swallow or two more of the brandy, he began to pick up visibly, sat straighter up, spoke louder and clearer, and looked in every way another man.

The breeze served us admirably. We skimmed before it like a bird, the coast of the island flashing by, and the view changing every minute. Soon we were past the high lands and bowling beside low, sandy country, sparsely dotted with dwarf pines, and soon we were beyond that again, and had turned the corner of the rocky hill that ends the island on the north.

I was greatly elated with my new command, and pleased with the bright, sunshiny weather and these different prospects of the coast. I had now plenty of water and good things to eat, and my conscience,

which had smitten me hard for my desertion, was quieted by the great conquest I had made. I should, I think, have had nothing left me to desire but for the eyes of the coxswain as they followed me derisively about the deck, and the odd smile that appeared continually on his face. It was a smile that had in it something both of pain and weakness—a haggard, old man's smile; but there was, besides that, a grin of derision, a shadow of treachery in his expression as he craftily watched, and watched, and watched me at my work.

The wind, serving us to a desire, now hauled into the west. We could run so much the easier from the northeast corner of the island to the mouth of the North Inlet. Only, as we had no power to anchor, and dared not beach her till the tide had flowed a good deal farther, time hung on our hands. The coxswain told me how to lay the ship to; after a good many trials I succeeded, and we both sat in silence, over another meal.

"Cap'n," said he, at length, with that same uncomfortable smile, "here's my old shipmate, O'Brien; s'pose you was to heave him overboard. I ain't partic'lar as a rule, and I don't take no blame for settling his hash; but I don't reckon him ornamental, now, do you?"

"I'm not strong enough, and I don't like the job; and there he lies for me," said I.

"This here's an unlucky ship—this *Hispaniola*, Jim," he went on, blinking. "There's a power of men been killed in this *Hispaniola*—a sight o' poor seamen dead and gone since you and me took ship to Bristol. I never seen sich dirty luck, not I. There was this here O'Brien, now—he's dead, ain't he? Well, now, I'm no scholar, and you're a lad as can read and figure; and, to put it straight, do you take it as a dead man is dead for good, or do he come alive again?"

"You can kill the body, Mr. Hands, but not the spirit; you must know that already," I replied. "O'Brien there is in another world, and maybe watching us."

"Ah!" says he. "Well, that's unfort'nate—appears as if killing parties was a waste of time. Howsomever, sperrits don't reckon for much, by what I've seen. I'll chance it with the sperrits, Jim. And now, you've spoke up free, and I'll take it kind if you'd step down into that there cabin and get me a—well, a—shiver my timbers! I can't hit the name on't; well, you get me a bottle of wine, Jim—this here brandy's too strong for my head."

Now, the coxswain's hesitation seemed to be unnatural; and as for the notion of his preferring wine to brandy, I entirely disbelieved it. The whole story was a pretext. He wanted me to leave the deck—so much was plain; but with what purpose I could in no way imagine. His eyes never met mine; they kept wandering to and fro, up and down, now with a look to the sky, now with a flitting glance upon the dead O'Brien. All the time he kept smiling, and putting his tongue out in the most guilty, embarrassed manner, so that a child could have told that he was bent on some deception. I was prompt with my answer, however, for I saw where my advantage lay; and that with a fellow so densely stupid I could easily conceal my suspicions to the end.

"Some wine?" said I. "Far better. Will you have white or red?"

"Well, I reckon it's about the blessed same to me, shipmate," he replied; "so it's strong, and plenty of it, what's the odds?"

"All right," I answered. "I'll bring you port, Mr. Hands. But I'll have to dig for it."

With that I scuttled down the companion with all the noise I could, slipped off my shoes, ran quietly along the sparred gallery, mounted the forecastle ladder, and

popped my head out of the fore companion. I knew he
would not expect to see me there; yet I took every
precaution possible; and certainly the worst of my
suspicions proved too true.

He had risen from his position to his hands and
knees; and, though his leg obviously hurt him pretty
sharply when he moved—for I could hear him stifle a
groan—yet it was at a good, rattling rate that he
trailed himself across the deck. In half a minute he
had reached the port scuppers, and picked, out of a coil
of rope, a long knife, or rather a short dirk, discoloured
to the hilt with blood. He looked upon it for a moment,
thrusting forth his under jaw, tried the point upon his
hand, and then, hastily concealing it in the bosom of
his jacket, trundled back again into his old place
against the bulwark.

This was all that I required to know. Israel could move about; he was now armed; and if he had been at so much trouble to get rid of me, it was plain that I was meant to be the victim. What he would do afterwards—whether he would try to crawl right across the island from North Inlet to the camp among the swamps, or whether he would fire Long Tom,[5] trusting that his own comrades might come first to help him, was, of course, more than I could say.

Yet I felt sure that I could trust him in one point, since in that our interests jumped together, and that was in the disposition of the schooner. We both desired to have her stranded safe enough, in a sheltered place, and so that, when the time came, she could be got off again with as little labour and danger as might be; and until that was done I considered that my life would certainly be spared.

While I was thus turning the business over in my mind, I had not been idle with my body. I had stolen back to the cabin, slipped once more into my shoes, and laid my hand at random on a bottle of wine, and now, with this for an excuse, I made my reappearance on the deck.

Hands lay as I had left him, all fallen together in a bundle, and with his eyelids lowered, as though he were too weak to bear the light. He looked up, however, at my coming, knocked the neck off the bottle, like a man who had done the same thing often, and took a good swig, with his favourite toast of "Here's luck!" Then he lay quiet for a little, and then, pulling out a stick of tobacco, begged me to cut him a quid.

"Cut me a junk o' that," says he, "for I haven't no knife, and hardly strength enough, so be as I had. Ah,

---

5. "Long Tom" was the name given the single small cannon that the ship carried.

Jim, Jim, I reckon I've missed stays! Cut me a quid, as'll likely be the last, lad; for I'm for my long home, and no mistake."

"Well," said I, "I'll cut you some tobacco; but if I was you and thought myself so badly, I would go to my prayers, like a Christian man."

"Why?" said he. "Now, you tell me why."

"Why?" I cried. "You were asking me just now about the dead. You've broken your trust; you've lived in sin and lies and blood; there's a man you killed lying at your feet this moment; and you ask me why! For God's mercy, Mr. Hands, that's why."

I spoke with a little heat, thinking of the bloody dirk he had hidden in his pocket, and designed, in his ill thoughts, to end me with. He, for his part, took a great draught of the wine, and spoke with the most unusual solemnity.

"For thirty years," he said, "I've sailed the seas, and seen good and bad, better and worse, fair weather and foul, provisions running out, knives going, and what not. Well, now I tell you, I never seen good come o' goodness yet. Him as strikes first is my fancy; dead men don't bite; them's my views—amen, so be it. And now, you look here," he added, suddenly changing his tone, "we've had about enough of this foolery. The tide's made good enough by now. You just take my orders, Cap'n Hawkins, and we'll sail slap in and be done with it."

All told, we had scarce two miles to run; but the navigation was delicate, the entrance to this northern anchorage was not only narrow and shoal, but lay east and west, so that the schooner must be nicely handled to be got in. I think I was a good, prompt subaltern, and I am very sure that Hands was an excellent pilot; for we went about and about, and dodged in, shaving the banks, with a certainty and a neatness that were a pleasure to behold.

Scarcely had we passed the heads before the land closed around us. The shores of North Inlet were as thickly wooded as those of the southern anchorage; but the space was longer and narrower, and more like, what in truth it was, the estuary of a river. Right before us, at the southern end, we saw the wreck of a ship in the last stages of dilapidation. It had been a great vessel of three masts, but had lain so long exposed to the injuries of the weather, that it was hung about with great webs of dripping seaweed, and on the deck of it shore bushes had taken root, and now flourished thick with flowers. It was a sad sight, but it showed us that the anchorage was calm.

"Now," said Hands, "look there; there's a pet bit for to beach a ship in. Fine flat sand, never a catspaw, trees all around of it, and flowers a-blowing like a garding on that old ship."

"And once beached," I inquired, "how shall we get her off again?"

"Why, so," he replied: "you take a line ashore there on the other side at low water: take a turn about one o' them big pines; bring it back, take a turn round the capstan, and lie-to for the tide. Come high water, all hands take a pull upon the line, and off she comes as sweet as natur'. And now, boy, you stand by. We're near the bit now, and she's too much way on her. Starboard a little—so—steady—starboard—larboard a little—steady—steady!"

So he issued his commands, which I breathlessly obeyed; till, all of a sudden, he cried, "Now, my hearty, luff!" And I put the helm hard up, and the *Hispaniola* swung round rapidly, and ran stem on for the low wooded shore.

The excitement of these last manoeuvres had somewhat interfered with the watch I had kept hitherto, sharply enough, upon the coxswain. Even then I was still so much interested, waiting for the ship to touch, that I had quite forgot the peril that hung over my head, and stood craning over the starboard bulwarks and watching the ripples spreading wide before the bows. I might have fallen without a struggle for my life, had not a sudden disquietude seized upon me, and made me turn my head. Perhaps I had heard a creak, or seen his shadow moving with the tail of my eye; perhaps it was an instinct like a cat's; but, sure enough, when I looked round, there was Hands, already half-way towards me, with the dirk in his right hand.

We must both have cried out aloud when our eyes met; but while mine was the shrill cry of terror, his was a roar of fury like a charging bull's. At the same instant he threw himself forward, and I leaped sideways towards the bows. As I did so, I let go of the tiller, which sprang sharp to leeward; and I think this saved my life, for it struck Hands across the chest, and stopped him, for the moment, dead.

Before he could recover, I was safe out of the corner where he had me trapped, with all the deck to dodge about. Just forward of the main-mast I stopped, drew a pistol from my pocket, took a cool aim, though he had already turned and was once more coming directly after me, and drew the trigger. The hammer fell, but there followed neither flash nor sound; the priming was useless with sea-water. I cursed myself for my neglect. Why had not I, long before, reprimed and reloaded my only weapons? Then I should not have been as now, a mere fleeing sheep before this butcher.

Wounded as he was, it was wonderful how fast he could move, his grizzled hair tumbling over his face, and his face itself as red as a red ensign with his haste and fury. I had no time to try my other pistol,

nor, indeed, much inclination, for I was sure it would be useless. One thing I saw plainly: I must not simply retreat before him, or he would speedily hold me boxed into the bows, as a moment since he had so nearly boxed me in the stern. Once so caught, and nine or ten inches of the blood-stained dirk would be my last experience on this side of eternity. I placed my palms against the main-mast, which was of a goodish bigness, and waited, every nerve upon the stretch.

Seeing that I meant to dodge, he also paused; and a moment or two passed in feints on his part, and corresponding movements upon mine. It was such a game as I had often played at home about the rocks of Black Hill Cove; but never before, you may be sure, with such a wildly beating heart as now. Still, as I say, it was a boy's game, and I thought I could hold my own at it, against an elderly seaman with a wounded thigh. Indeed, my courage had begun to rise so high, that I allowed myself a few darting thoughts on what would be the end of the affair; and while I saw certainly that I could spin it out for long, I saw no hope of any ultimate escape.

Well, while things stood thus, suddenly the *Hispaniola* struck, staggered, ground for an instant in the sand, and then, swift as a blow, canted over to the port side, till the deck stood at an angle of forty-five degrees, and about a puncheon[6] of water splashed into the scupper holes, and lay, in a pool, between the deck and bulwark.

We were both of us capsized in a second, and both of us rolled, almost together, into the scuppers; the dead red-cap, with his arms still spread out, tumbling stiffly after us. So near were we, indeed, that my head came against the coxswain's foot with a crack that made my teeth rattle. Blow and all, I was the first afoot again; for Hands had got involved with the dead body. The sudden canting of the ship had made the deck no place

---

6. A puncheon (PUHN chuhn) is a large cask, and also a unit of measure equal to 84 gallons (318 liters).

for running on; I had to find some new way of escape,
and that upon the instant, for my foe was almost
touching me. Quick as thought, I sprang into the
mizzen shrouds, rattled up hand over hand, and did not
draw a breath till I was seated on the cross-trees.

I had been saved by being prompt; the dirk had
struck not half a foot below me, as I pursued my
upward flight; and there stood Israel Hands with his
mouth open and his face upturned to mine, a perfect
statue of surprise and disappointment.

Now that I had a moment to myself, I lost no time
in changing the priming of my pistol, and then, having

one ready for service, and to make assurance doubly
sure, I proceeded to draw the load of the other, and
recharge it afresh from the beginning.

My new employment struck Hands all of a heap; he
began to see the dice going against him; and, after an
obvious hesitation, he also hauled himself heavily into
the shrouds, and, with the dirk in his teeth, began
slowly and painfully to mount. It cost him no end of
time and groans to haul his wounded leg behind him;
and I had quietly finished my arrangements before he
was much more than a third of the way up. Then, with
a pistol in either hand, I addressed him.

"One more step, Mr. Hands," said I, "and I'll blow your brains out! Dead men don't bite, you know," I added, with a chuckle.

He stopped instantly. I could see by the working of his face that he was trying to think, and the process was so slow and laborious that, in my new-found security, I laughed aloud. At last, with a swallow or two, he spoke, his face still wearing the same expression of extreme perplexity. In order to speak he had to take the dagger from his mouth, but, in all else, he remained unmoved.

"Jim," says he, "I reckon we're fouled, you and me, and we'll have to sign articles. I'd have had you but for that there lurch: but I don't have no luck, not I; and I reckon I'll have to strike, which comes hard, you see, for a master mariner to a ship's younker like you, Jim."

I was drinking in his words and smiling away, as conceited as a cock upon a wall, when, all in a breath, back went his right hand over his shoulder. Something sang like an arrow through the air; I felt a blow and then a sharp pang, and there I was pinned by the shoulder to the mast. In the horrid pain and surprise of the moment—I scarce can say it was by my own volition, and I am sure it was without a conscious aim—both my pistols went off, and both escaped out of my hands. They did not fall alone; with a choked cry, the coxswain loosed his grasp upon the shrouds, and plunged head first into the water.

If this small part of *Treasure Island* has given you a taste for adventure, read the whole book. It is excitement from beginning to end. And then you might try *Silver's Revenge* by Robert Leeson, which is all about what happened to those few who survived the voyage of the *Hispaniola*.

Haiku

Haiku is a Japanese verse form consisting of seventeen syllables arranged in three unrhymed lines of five, seven, and five syllables each. However, this syllable scheme often varies in translation.

About three hundred years ago, the great Japanese poet Matsuo Bashō raised haiku to a serious art form written according to strict rules. Haiku had to describe subjects in nature and contain a reference to a season of the year. After you have read these verses, try writing some of your own haiku.

Far across hill and dale
The blossoms of the plum have cast
    A delicate pink veil.

Bashō

A mountain village
deep in snow ... under the drifts
    a sound of water.

Shiki

Get out of my road
And allow me to plant these
    Bamboos, Mr. Toad!

Chora

In spite of cold and chills
That usher in the early spring
    We have the daffodils.

Kikuriō

When my canary
Flew away, that was the end
    Of spring in my house.

Shiki

The sunrise tints the dew;
The yellow crocuses are out,
    And I must pick a few.

Jōsa

In spring the chirping
Frogs sing like birds ... in summer
    They bark like old dogs.

Onitsura

The lost child cries,
And as he cries, he clutches
    At the fireflies.

Ryusui

I came to look, and lo,
The plum tree petals scatter down
    A fall of purest snow.

Reinkō

I must go begging
for water ... morning glories
have captured my well.

Chiyo

How cool cut hay smells
when carried through the farm gate
as the sun comes up!

Boncho

What a wonderful
day! No one in the village
doing anything.

Shiki

Under the willow
With a leaf stuck in his mouth
The puppy sleeps.

Issa

265

The Minstrel-Boy
by Thomas Moore

The Minstrel-boy to the war is gone,
   In the ranks of death you'll find him;
His father's sword he has girded on,
   And his wild harp slung behind him.—
"Land of song!" said the warrior-bard,
   "Though all the world betrays thee,
One sword, at least, thy rights shall guard,
   One faithful harp shall praise thee!"

The Minstrel fell! But the foeman's chain
   Could not bring his proud soul under;
The harp he loved ne'er spoke again,
   For he tore its cords asunder;
And said "No chains shall sully thee,
   Thou soul of love and bravery!
Thy songs were made for the brave and free,
   They shall never sound in slavery!"

The Harp That Once Through Tara's Halls
by Thomas Moore

The harp that once through Tara's halls
   The soul of beauty shed,
Now hangs as mute on Tara's walls,
   As if that soul were fled.—
So sleeps the pride of former days,
   So glory's thrill is o'er,
And hearts that once beat high for praise,
   Now feel that pulse no more.

No more to chiefs and ladies bright
   The harp of Tara swells;
The chord alone, that breaks at night,
   Its tale of ruin tells.
Thus Freedom now so seldom wakes,
   The only throb she gives,
Is when some heart indignant breaks,
   To show that still she lives.

The Challenge

from *Sea Glass*
by Laurence Yep

Craig is a Chinese-American boy who has lived in San
Francisco's Chinatown all his life. Then, when he is in
eighth grade, his family moves back to the small
coastal town where his father grew up. Craig is not
very popular. He is overweight, awkward, and no good
at sports. He is also too Chinese for his Americanized
cousins and too American for the old Chinese man
who becomes his friend.

✿ ✿ ✿

I wasn't very comfortable with any of the old-timers.
But the one old-timer who really got to me was this
spooky one I never got to see for week after week. His
name was Uncle *Quail*. Of all the grocery deliveries I
had to make, going to his cottage was the longest and
the hardest trip, so I always delivered his groceries
last in the afternoon.

I thought of Uncle *Quail* as some kind of ogre after
Uncle Lester's stories. Uncle Lester, who actually
owned the Victory Grocery Store, was only a friend of
Dad's and no blood relation to us; but he had said that

his uncle *Quail* was a blood relative—something like a great-uncle or even a great-great-great-uncle. Uncle *Quail* had always been here as far as Uncle Lester knew, and Uncle *Quail* had always been one of the store's liabilities—like the mortgage, the leaking roof, and the mice. You see, Uncle *Quail* received his groceries for free.

Every week I brought him the same things from the list. There were cans of peas and soup, and a small bag of rice, and other things like sardines and seven cigars. Uncle always wanted yams—fresh when they were in season, otherwise he took canned ones. There also had to be a freshly killed chicken. Uncle Lester had instructed Dad to pay a nearby farmer special to bring in a freshly killed chicken every week. Dad had to pluck and clean it, though.

Anyway, during all those months I had been delivering Uncle's groceries, I was kind of grateful that he hadn't come out to talk to me.

Then came that one Saturday in April.

It started out like any other trip. First, I had to go through the part of town that was one of the oldest; the street was shaded by big poplar trees whose roots tilted up the sidewalk sections so that the slabs looked like the waves of a stormy sea that had been frozen suddenly. It wasn't any fun pulling the wagon up and down the slabs of sidewalk. But the fun really began when the sidewalk came to an end, and I had to pull the wagon along the dirt road.

When I reached the cliffs, I stopped and took a breath before I started up the sandy path that zigzagged to the top. A dirt track led across the top of the cliffs, and I pulled the wagon along past the brown weeds and the scraggly windblown trees that grew there. I stopped by the old rusty wire-mesh fence. The gate was unlocked, as it always was on Saturdays. The open padlock hung to the side on one of the wires.

Carefully I lowered the wagon down the stone path
to Uncle's house. Uncle lived on a small cove about
fifty feet across that was formed by the cliffs and a
headland. The rock had crumbled at the mouth of the
cove a long time ago, maybe in some storm when the
heavy waves had come crashing in, and now lay piled
across it to form a reef that protected the cove from
the rest of the sea—except for that one narrow
opening in the reef. Right now it must have been high
tide, because only the top of the reef showed.

There was only a little strip of beach at high tide,
and I couldn't see the wooden pilings where Uncle used
to have a small wharf. A stone path wound up the cliff
wall behind the beach for about fifty feet before the
path widened out to a ledge about thirty by forty feet.
It was there that Uncle had built his little wooden
cottage. The paint had worn off long ago, leaving the
wooden planks exposed to the wind and the salt spray
so that the wood was a grayish color and smooth as
the surface of a skull.

There were shades over the windows, shades so old
that they looked an orange-goldish color. Sometimes I
thought I saw one of the shades stir—like an eyelid
twitching. And I would have this spooky feeling like
someone was watching me.

I would always shove the new carton of groceries and bunch of the past week's Chinese newspapers onto the porch. Then I'd take the old box, which was filled with garbage that Uncle had wrapped neatly in last week's newspapers. I'd put the box into the wagon and I'd tear back up the path with the almost-empty wagon rattling and bumping along behind me.

But today it was different.

I had just put the carton of groceries on the porch of Uncle's house when the door suddenly opened and an elderly Chinese in his seventies stood there.

On his feet he had a pair of Chinese slippers with dragons embroidered on the front. His legs were encased in a pair of old gray work pants that sagged like elephant legs. Over a torn T-shirt, Uncle wore an

old green jacket that came only to his waist. The lining on the inside obviously had once been of bright bands of yellow, red, and green in some silklike material, but the coat was torn now at the bottom, and though Uncle *Quail* had tried to mend it, the material had been too old and worn, so that his jacket had torn again, letting the padding begin to trail out once more.

He held out his hand to me and said something in Chinese, but too quickly for me to understand. Then he spoke more slowly, barely able to contain his impatience.

"Quick, boy. I want the sardines." The last word was in American.

When I just stared at him, he gave a little contemptuous sigh and dug around in the carton himself, scattering cans left and right onto the porch. I looked over the railing down at the cove fifty feet below his house. A small shadow circled underneath the surface of the water.

"What's that?" I asked in Chinese. I turned back to Uncle. He had pried the key off the bottom of the can and fitted it onto the metal tab on the top. Then he began to wind the entire lid down.

In the meantime, the creature had surfaced so I could see it was an otter. He stared at us for a moment; then he began to clown in the water, rolling and spiraling and tumbling.

"Quit showing off," Uncle pretended to scold the otter. With a flick of his wrist, Uncle threw a fish up high into the air. It glittered as it fell through the sunny afternoon air: a silvery flake that splashed into the water near the otter's head. The otter dove, surfacing to float on his back with the fish between his humanlike paws. He ate with big nods of his head as he gulped it down.

Uncle wiped his fingers on the seat of his pants and glanced at me. *"You want to try it?"* He held the can in front of me. I slipped a sardine out and threw it. It

almost hit the otter on the stomach. He looked so surprised and indignant that Uncle and I both had to laugh. It didn't seem to bother the otter, though, because he dove for the fish. We took turns feeding him after that. The otter seemed to realize when the tin was empty, because he began to circle the cove.

I watched him slide around in the water. It was hard to think of him as flesh and bone. He curled around so fast and darted away that he seemed more like a brown streak that someone was trying to paint on the water, only the water kept on shrugging off the paint. It almost hurt inside me to look at him. That otter was so sleek and fast and graceful—everything I had ever wanted to be and wasn't. I held on to the porch railing so I could lean far out to catch one last glimpse as he shot through the narrow opening in the reef at the mouth of the cove and out into the open sea. And then I couldn't see him anymore.

Uncle said something more in Chinese.

"Pardon me?" I asked.

Uncle spoke in American. "I said he's very

beautiful." He switched back to Chinese. *"What's the matter: Don't you speak the language of the T'ang people?"*

"Only a little," I confessed. I waited for him to begin ranting like Ah Joe had done.

Uncle grunted like he wasn't surprised in the least at my stupidity. "You speak. You act. You even think like a *white demon*." By *demon*, he meant an American. With a very stern expression on his face, he stared at me.

I was more intimidated by Uncle than I had been by Ah Joe. Though Uncle *Quail* was in his seventies, he still moved quickly and yet gracefully—as if his body could barely contain all of his energy. His hair, which he cut short on top and almost shaved on the sides and back of his head, only accented the bullet shape of his skull. His shoulders were still broad and heavily muscled.

"Well, *little demon*, someone squeezes my bread too much." He made wringing motions with his hands as if he were twisting the water out of a wet towel. "Is it you?"

"I guess I just grab it too hard when I'm in a hurry." I rubbed nervously at a patch of dirt I'd gotten somehow on my left elbow.

"I only make toast with it anyway," Uncle said, "but I don't want toast that is all twisted. How you like it if I pay you with bent coins, hunh?"

"I'll be more careful the next time," I promised.

"I wait and see." Uncle clasped his hands behind his back. "What's your name, boy?"

"Craig. Craig Chin."

"Ah." Uncle scratched for a moment behind his ear. "Are you Calvin's son?"

"Yes, sir."

"He and Lester, they used to bring my groceries. Just like you, hah?" He waved his hand back and forth between me and him. "But that was a long, long time ago." Uncle paused as if he were searching for something else to say. "Your father was strong. Even when he was small. Very strong." Uncle closed his hands into fists and pretended to make his muscles bulge. "He always play the *demon* games even then."

Even down here I couldn't escape from Dad's reputation. "Oh" was all I said.

"And you? You like the *demon* games?" Uncle asked kindly.

"Sort of," I said without much enthusiasm. Somehow, whenever I got to talking to people about my dad, they always wound up asking me if I liked sports. They assumed not only that I did, but that I would be as good at them as Dad had been. I went on quickly. "But I'm not very good at sports." I glanced at the box with Uncle's garbage neatly wrapped in newspaper and began to think of excuses for leaving.

But instead of going on with his questions as other people would have done, Uncle was silent. When I turned around to say good-bye to him, I found him studying me. There was a fine network of wrinkles around his eyes, but I hadn't noticed them before because his face had been more or less relaxed. Now, though, his forehead was wrinkled and his eyebrows were drawn together, and there was a deep, intense look to his eyes. For a moment, I felt more alive: as if I ought to be like the sunlight leaping from the back of one ocean wave to another.

Then Uncle blinked his eyes and the look slipped away from his face. He smiled at me reassuringly. I felt the corners of my mouth turn up into a brief, uneasy grin. It was as if Uncle understood that I didn't want to be asked any more questions about how good I was at sports.

For a long time, neither of us knew what to say to the other. Finally Uncle faced toward the cove. "You . . . you like my friend?"

I could only nod my head in agreement. We had something to share after all. I think that fact pleased the both of us. "Does the otter come here often?"

"That lazy thing? He only comes when he feels like it. One of these days, no more fine meals from me." Uncle did his best to sound as if he disapproved of the otter because he begged for food. It was actually, as I was to learn, just Uncle's way never to compliment anything wholeheartedly. Uncle added sternly, "It's a waste of good food."

Even so, I knew he ordered two cans of sardines every week, because I was the one who filled his order for groceries. It was written on a scrap of butcher paper in pencil that had gotten smudged over the months. I suppose Uncle had dictated the list to his relative, Uncle Lester.

"Will the otter be back today?" I asked Uncle.

Uncle scratched the side of his nose. "I not think so." He added, as if he didn't know what to do with me, "But you can wait if you want."

"I guess I could stay a little while." I sat down on the porch and began to pick up the cans that Uncle had scattered all around while he had been hunting for one of the sardine cans. As neatly as I could, I put the cans back into the carton.

Uncle picked up the seven cigars from the porch where he had tossed them earlier. Then he sat down carefully on the porch beside me. He stretched one leg out stiffly and rubbed it as if it ached. With his other hand, he stowed six of the cigars into a jacket pocket. Finally he unwrapped the seventh cigar and bit off one end, spitting out the little mouthful. Then he reversed the cigar and stuck it into his mouth. Clenching it between his teeth, he hunted around in his pants pocket and took out a book of matches. His other hand groped around on the porch until it found a black ugly shell by the left railing. The shell was about

seven inches long. But when he turned it over, I saw
the inside was all silvery, with a beautiful swirl of
metallic colors rippling and flowing around the insides
as if this were half of a shell that had hatched a
rainbow.

While he lit his cigar, I studied the shell in
fascination. "Where did you get that?"

"This?" Uncle held up the shell as if he took it for
granted. "It's only an abalone shell. No good. Got too
many cracks."

"I've eaten abalone. I thought they were fish."

"No, boy." Uncle laughed. He waved his cigar toward
the cliff. "In the old days there was a whole bunch of
us catching abalone south by Monterey. We cut the
meat and put it on trays so the meat dries. Then we
send the meat to China. We sell the shells, too. Some
months you could shut your eyes and just smell the

air." Uncle closed his eyes and pretended to sniff at the air. "And you find our camp."

With great care, Uncle slowly took the cigar from his mouth so that the ash stayed there until he could tap his cigar against the side of the abalone shell—it was as if he were playing a game with himself. "Hey, you know what, boy?" He glanced at me sideways. "I find abalone on my reef still." He jabbed his cigar at the air in the direction of the reef. "Someday I take you out there and we dive for abalone." He added, "But you think you could keep it a secret? I don't want everyone down here." He turned and looked at me shrewdly.

"I can keep a secret," I said doubtfully, "but do we really have to swim out there?"

Uncle grunted. "Maybe I see how well you swim. The abalone, they don't come crawling into your hand, you know." Uncle was doing his best to sound disinterested, but I could hear the eagerness in his voice.

Even so, I hesitated. "I don't know." I didn't want to disappoint Uncle, and yet I didn't know how to tell him that I found it embarrassing to go swimming. Once, when we were still in San Francisco, I'd gone to Ocean Beach with some friends, and I felt real stupid there. I'm fat. I wore an extra-big T-shirt to cover up my stomach. And my swimming trunks were large ones and they hung down almost to my knees. I felt like all the average, thin people were looking at me and snickering.

Uncle sucked at his cigar and then blew out a large circle. "Don't you worry, boy," he said gently. "Most of the time nobody comes up here, so nobody can see us." It was as if he could read my mind. Sometimes you meet people who like having other people around so they can have an excuse to hear their own voices talking. But as I came to know Uncle, I found that he could understand people—almost as if he could read people's minds and didn't much like what he read there so he usually didn't make the effort. Uncle knocked some more ash into the shell. "You know, it's a funny thing, but I don't like people watching me. A few times people come up to the cliffs, but then I can smell them so I go inside."

I looked down at the seawater surging up the sand. It was like a thing alive, with gold scales winking and disappearing and reappearing again on the surface. And outside the cove I could see the separate shades of water in the sea. It certainly looked inviting.

But then I let myself imagine what Mom and Dad would say, especially Dad, when I gave them an abalone shell as a decoration for our house. Maybe if I had two, I could show one of the shells to the other kids. I could just picture the kids' faces.

"You do swim, don't you, boy?" Uncle asked.

"I learned in the pool at the Chinatown Y up in the City."

Uncle snorted in disgust. "That's tame water. Nothing to see but chlorine and the legs of other people kicking." He nodded toward his cove. "You take a place like this. Now that's water."

I held on to the railing. "It might be fun to swim here. If it's okay."

"Oh-kay." Uncle made it sound like two separate words. "Next Saturday, when you bring my food." He gave an almost shy little smile.

Do you think that Craig will face up to the challenge Uncle *Quail* has set for him? You can find out by reading the rest of *Sea Glass*. You might also like to read two other books by Laurence Yep: *Child of the Owl*, which is about a Chinese-American girl named Casey, and *Dragonwings*, a story about a Chinese boy who goes to live with his father in America.

The Shooting-Match at Nottingham Town

from *The Merry Adventures of Robin Hood*
by Howard Pyle

Robin Hood was a legendary English outlaw and expert
archer who robbed the rich and gave to the poor. He
and his merry band of followers lived in Sherwood
Forest, near Nottingham. In the tale that follows, the
evil Sheriff of Nottingham thinks of a plan that he is
sure will enable him to capture Robin Hood.

❦ ❦ ❦

The Sheriff bade all his servants and retainers to
make ready to go to London Town, to see and speak
with the King.

At this there was bustling at the Sheriff's castle,
and men ran hither and thither upon this business and
upon that, while the forge fires of Nottingham glowed
red far into the night like twinkling stars, for all the
smiths of the town were busy making or mending
armor for the Sheriff's troop of escort. For two days

this labor lasted, then, on the third, all was ready for the journey. So forth they started in the bright sunlight, from Nottingham Town to Fosse Way and thence to Watling Street; and so they journeyed for two days, until they saw at last the spires and towers of great London Town; and many folks stopped, as they journeyed along, and gazed at the show they made riding along the highways with their flashing armor, and gay plumes and trappings.

In London King Henry and his fair Queen Eleanor held their court, gay with ladies in silks and satins and velvets and cloth of gold, and also brave knights and gallant courtiers.

Thither came the Sheriff and was shown into the King's presence.

"A boon, a boon," quoth he, as he knelt upon the ground.

"Now what wouldst thou have?" said the King. "Let us hear what may be thy desires."

"O good my Lord and Sovereign," spake the Sheriff, "in Sherwood Forest in our own good shire of Nottingham, liveth a bold outlaw whose name is Robin Hood."

"In good sooth," said the King, "his doings have reached even our own royal ears. He is a saucy, rebellious varlet, yet, I am fain to own, a right merry soul withal."

"But hearken, O my most gracious Sovereign," said the Sheriff. "I sent a warrant to him with thine own royal seal attached, by a right lusty knave, but he beat the messenger and stole the warrant. And he killeth thy deer and robbeth thine own liege subjects[1] even upon the great highways."

"Why, how now," quoth the King, wrathfully. "What wouldst thou have me do? Comest thou not to me with

---

1. Liege subjects are those people who are obliged to honor and give loyal service to a lord or king.

a great array of men-at-arms and retainers, and yet art not able to take a single band of lusty knaves without armor on breast, in thine own county! What wouldst thou have me do? Art thou not my Sheriff? Are not my laws in force in Nottinghamshire? Canst thou not take thine own course against those that break the laws or do any injury to thee or thine? Go, get thee gone, and think well; devise some plan of thine own but trouble me no further. But look well to it, master Sheriff, for I will have my laws obeyed by all men within my kingdom, and if thou art not able to enforce them thou art no sheriff for me. So look well to thyself, I say, or ill may befall thee as well as all the thieving knaves in Nottinghamshire. When the flood cometh it sweepeth away grain as well as chaff."

Then the Sheriff turned away with a sore and troubled heart, and sadly he rued his fine show of retainers, for he saw that the King was angry because he had so many men about him and yet could not enforce the laws. So, as they all rode slowly back to Nottingham, the Sheriff was thoughtful and full of care. Not a word did he speak to any one, and no one of his men spoke to him, but all the time he was busy devising some plan to take Robin Hood.

"Now," thought the Sheriff, "could I but persuade Robin nigh to Nottingham Town so that I could find him, I warrant I would lay hands upon him so stoutly that he would never get away again." Then of a sudden it came to him like a flash that were he to proclaim a great shooting-match and offer some grand prize, Robin Hood might be over-persuaded by his spirit to come to the butts.[2]

So, as soon as he had returned safely to Nottingham, he sent messengers north and south, and east and west, to proclaim through town, hamlet, and

---

2. The butts is the area where the targets will be set up.

countryside, this grand shooting-match, and every one was bidden that could draw a long bow, and the prize was to be an arrow of pure beaten gold.

When Robin Hood first heard the news of this he was in Lincoln Town, and hastening back to Sherwood Forest he soon called all his merry men about him and spoke to them thus:—

"Now hearken, my merry men all, to the news that I have brought from Lincoln Town today. Our friend the Sheriff of Nottingham hath proclaimed a shooting-match, and hath sent messengers to tell of it through all the countryside, and the prize is to be a bright golden arrow. Now I fain would have one of us win it, both because of the fairness of the prize and because our sweet friend the Sheriff hath offered it. So we will take our bows and shafts and go there to shoot, for I know right well that merriment will be a-going. What say ye, lads?"

Then young David of Doncaster spoke up and said: "Now listen, I pray thee, good master, unto what I say. I have come straight from our friend Eadom o' the Blue Boar, and there I heard the full news of this same match. But, master, I know from him, and he got it

from the Sheriff's man Ralph o' the Scar, that this same knavish Sheriff hath but laid a trap for thee in this shooting-match and wishes nothing so much as to see thee there. So go not, good master, for I know right well he doth seek to beguile thee, but stay within the greenwood lest we all meet dole and woe."

"Now," quoth Robin, "thou art a wise lad and keepest thine ears open and thy mouth shut, as becometh a wise and crafty woodsman. But shall we let it be said that the Sheriff of Nottingham did cow bold Robin Hood and sevenscore[3] as fair archers as are in all merry England? Nay, good David, what thou tellest me maketh me to desire the prize even more than I else should do. But what sayeth our good gossip Swanthold? is it not 'A hasty man burneth his mouth, and the fool that keepeth his eyes shut falleth into the pit'? Thus he says, truly, therefore we must meet guile with guile. Now some of you clothe yourselves as curtal friars,[4] and some as rustic peasants, and some as tinkers,[5] or as beggars, but see that each man taketh a good bow or broadsword, in case need should arise. As for myself, I will shoot for this same golden arrow, and should I win it, we will hang it to the branches of our good greenwood tree for the joy of all the band. How like you the plan, my merry men all?"

Then "good, good!" cried all the band right heartily.

A fair sight was Nottingham Town on the day of the shooting-match. All along upon the green meadow beneath the town wall stretched a row of benches, one above the other, which were for knight and lady, squire and dame, and rich burghers[6] and their wives; for none but those of rank and quality were to sit

---

3. A score is a group or set of twenty, so sevenscore would be 7 x 20 or 140.
4. A friar is a man belonging to one of certain religious brotherhoods in the Roman Catholic Church. A curtal friar is one who wears a short robe.
5. A tinker is a man who mends pots and pans.
6. A burgher is a citizen of a burgh or town.

there. At the end of the range, near the target, was a
raised seat bedecked with ribbons and scarfs and
garlands of flowers, for the Sheriff of Nottingham and
his dame. The range was twoscore paces broad.[7] At one
end stood the target, at the other a tent of striped
canvas, from the pole of which fluttered many-colored
flags and streamers. In this booth were casks of ale,
free to be broached by any of the archers who might
wish to quench their thirst.

Across the range from where the seats for the better
folk were raised was a railing to keep the poorer
people from crowding in front of the target. Already,

---

7. A pace is a step—a distance of about 2½ feet (0.8 meter). Twoscore
paces would be forty steps, so the range was about 100 feet (30.5 m) wide.

while it was early, the benches were beginning to fill with people of quality, who kept constantly arriving in little carts, or upon palfreys[8] that curveted gayly to the merry tinkle of silver bells at bridle reins; with these came also the poorer folk, who sat or lay upon the green grass near the railing that kept them from off the range. In the great tent the archers were gathering by twos and threes; some talking loudly of the fair shots each man had made in his day; some looking well to their bows, drawing a string betwixt the fingers to see that there was no fray upon it, or

---

8. A palfrey is a gentle riding horse.

inspecting arrows, shutting one eye and peering down a shaft to see that it was not warped, but straight and true, for neither bow nor shaft should fail at such a time and for such a prize. And never were such a company of yeomen[9] as were gathered at Nottingham Town that day, for the very best archers of merry England had come to this shooting-match. There was Gill o' the Red Cap, the Sheriff's own head archer, and Diccon Cruikshank of Lincoln Town, and Adam o' the Dell, a man of Tamworth, of threescore years and more, yet hale and lusty still, who in his time had shot in the famous match at Woodstock, and had there beaten that renowned archer, Clym o' the Clough. And many more famous men of the long bow were there, whose names have been handed down to us in goodly ballads of the olden time.

But now all the benches were filled with guests, lord and lady, burgher and dame, when at last the Sheriff himself came with his lady, he riding with stately mien[10] upon his milk-white horse and she upon her brown filly. Upon his head he wore a purple velvet cap, and purple velvet was his robe, all trimmed about with rich ermine; his jerkin[11] and hose were of sea-green silk, and his shoes of black velvet, the pointed toes fastened to his garters with golden chains. A golden chain hung about his neck, and at his collar was a great carbuncle[12] set in red gold. His lady was dressed in blue velvet, all trimmed with swan's down. So they made a gallant sight as they rode along side by side, and all the people shouted from where they crowded across the space from the gentlefolk; so the Sheriff

---

9. A yeoman is a man who owns a small amount of land that he farms himself. The term is also used to describe a servant to a lord or an assistant to an official.
10. Mien is the way one holds one's head and body; one's bearing or appearance.
11. A jerkin is a short coat or jacket, with or without sleeves.
12. A carbuncle is a smooth, round garnet or other deep-red jewel.

and his lady came to their place, where men-at-arms,
with hauberk[13] and spear, stood about, waiting for
them.

Then when the Sheriff and his dame had sat down,
he bade his herald wind[14] upon his silver horn; who
thereupon sounded three blasts that came echoing
cheerily back from the gray walls of Nottingham. Then
the archers stepped forth to their places, while all the
folks shouted with a mighty voice, each man calling
upon his favorite yeoman. "Red Cap!" cried some;
"Cruikshank!" cried others; "Hey for William o'
Leslie!" shouted others yet again; while ladies waved
silken scarfs to urge each yeoman to do his best.

Then the herald stood forth and loudly proclaimed
the rules of the game as follows:—

"Shoot each man from yon mark, which is sevenscore
yards and ten[15] from the target. One arrow shooteth
each man first, and from all the archers shall the ten
that shooteth the fairest shafts be chosen for to shoot

---

13. A hauberk is a long coat of mail. Mail is flexible armor made of
metal rings, small loops of chain linked together, or of overlapping plates.
14. To wind means to blow.
15. Sevenscore yards and ten is 150 yards (137 m).

again. Two arrows shooteth each man of these ten, then shall the three that shoot the fairest shafts be chosen for to shoot again. Three arrows shooteth each man of those three, and to him that shooteth the fairest shafts shall the prize be given."

Then the Sheriff leaned forward, looking keenly among the press of archers to find whether Robin Hood was amongst them; but no one was there clad in Lincoln green, such as was worn by Robin and his band. "Nevertheless," said the Sheriff to himself, "he may still be there, and I miss him among the crowd of other men. But let me see when but ten men shoot, for I wot he will be among the ten, or I know him not."

And now the archers shot, each man in turn, and the good folk never saw such archery as was done that day. Six arrows were within the clout, four within the black, and only two smote the outer ring[16]; so that when the last arrow sped and struck the target, all the people shouted aloud, for it was noble shooting.

And now but ten men were left of all those that had shot before, and of these ten, six were famous throughout the land, and most of the folk gathered there knew them. These six men were Gilbert o' the Red Cap, Adam o' the Dell, Diccon Cruikshank, William o' Leslie, Hubert o' Cloud, and Swithin o' Hertford. Two others were yeomen of merry Yorkshire, another was a tall stranger in blue, who said he came from London Town, and the last was a tattered stranger in scarlet, who wore a patch over one eye.

"Now," quoth the Sheriff to a man-at-arms who stood near him, "seest thou Robin Hood amongst those ten?"

"Nay, that do I not, your worship," answered the man. "Six of them I know right well. Of those

---

16. The target was marked with scoring rings. The clout was the ring that included the center. The black was the ring outside the clout.

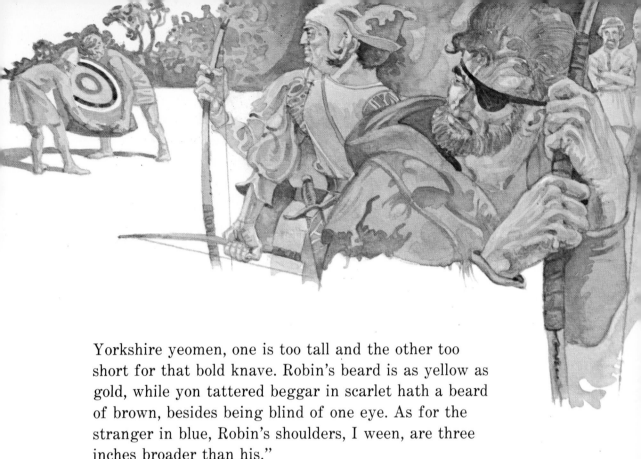

Yorkshire yeomen, one is too tall and the other too
short for that bold knave. Robin's beard is as yellow as
gold, while yon tattered beggar in scarlet hath a beard
of brown, besides being blind of one eye. As for the
stranger in blue, Robin's shoulders, I ween, are three
inches broader than his."

"Then," quoth the Sheriff, smiting his thigh angrily,
"yon knave is a coward as well as a rogue, and dares
not show his face among good men and true."

Then after they had rested a short time, those ten
stout men stepped forth to shoot again. Each man shot
two arrows, and as they shot, not a word was spoken,
but all the crowd watched with scarce a breath of
sound; but when the last had shot his arrow another
great shout arose, while many cast their caps aloft for
joy of such marvellous shooting.

"Now by our gracious Lady fair," quoth old Sir
Amyas o' the Dell, who, bowed with fourscore years
and more, sat near the Sheriff, "ne'er saw I such
archery in all my life before, yet have I seen the best
hands at the long bow for threescore years and more."

And now but three men were left of all those that
had shot before. One was Gill o' the Red Cap, one the
tattered stranger in scarlet, and one Adam o' the Dell

of Tamworth Town. Then all the people called aloud, some crying, "Ho for Gilbert o' the Red Cap!" and some, "Hey for stout Adam o' Tamworth!" but not a single man in the crowd called upon the stranger in scarlet.

"Now, shoot thou well, Gilbert," cried the Sheriff, "and if thine be the best shaft, fivescore broad silver pennies will I give to thee beside the prize."

"Truly I will do my best," quoth Gilbert, right sturdily. "A man cannot do aught but his best, but that will I strive to do this day." So saying, he drew forth a fair smooth arrow with a broad feather and fitted it deftly to the string, then drawing his bow with care he sped the shaft. Straight flew the arrow and lit fairly in the clout, a finger breadth from the centre. "A Gilbert, a Gilbert!" shouted all the crowd; and, "Now, by my faith," cried the Sheriff, smiting his hands together, "that is a shrewd shot."

Then the tattered stranger stepped forth, and all the people laughed as they saw a yellow patch that showed beneath his arm when he raised his elbow to shoot, and also to see him aim with but one eye. He drew the good yew bow quickly, and quickly loosed a shaft; so short was the time that no man could draw a breath betwixt the drawing and the shooting; yet his arrow lodged nearer the centre than the other by twice the length of a barleycorn.

"Now by all the saints in Paradise!" cried the Sheriff, "that is a lovely shaft in very truth!"

Then Adam o' the Dell shot, carefully and cautiously, and his arrow lodged close beside the stranger's. Then after a short space they all three shot again, and once more each arrow lodged within the clout, but this time Adam o' the Dell's was farthest from the centre, and again the tattered stranger's shot was the best. Then, after another time of rest, they all shot for the third time. This time Gilbert took great heed to his aim,

keenly measuring the distance and shooting with shrewdest care. Straight flew the arrow, and all shouted till the very flags that waved in the breeze shook with the sound, and the rooks and daws flew clamoring about the roofs of the old gray tower, for the shaft had lodged close beside the spot that marked the very centre.

"Well done, Gilbert!" cried the Sheriff, right joyously. "Fain am I to believe the prize is thine, and right fairly won. Now, thou ragged knave, let me see thee shoot a better shaft than that."

Naught spake the stranger but took his place, while all was hushed, and no one spoke or even seemed to breathe, so great was the silence for wonder what he would do. Meanwhile, also, quite still stood the stranger holding his bow in his hand, while one could count five; then he drew his trusty yew, holding it drawn but a moment, then loosed the string. Straight flew the arrow, and so true that it smote a gray goose feather from off Gilbert's shaft, which fell fluttering through the sunlit air as the stranger's arrow lodged close beside his of the Red Cap, and in the very centre. No one spoke a word for a while and no one shouted, but each man looked into his neighbor's face amazedly.

"Nay," quoth old Adam o' the Dell presently, drawing a long breath and shaking his head as he spoke; "twoscore years and more have I shot shaft, and maybe not all times bad, but I shoot no more this day, for no man can match with yon stranger, whosoe'er he may be." Then he thrust his shaft into his quiver, rattling, and unstrung his bow without another word.

Then the Sheriff came down from his dais[17] and drew near, in all his silks and velvets, to where the tattered stranger stood leaning upon his stout bow, whilst the good folk crowded around to see the man

---

17. A dais is a raised platform.

who shot so wondrously well. "Here, good fellow," quoth the Sheriff, "take thou the prize, and well and fairly hast thou won it, I trow. What may be thy name, and whence comest thou?"

"Men do call me Jock o' Teviotdale, and thence am I come," said the stranger.

"Then, by Our Lady, Jock, thou art the fairest archer that e'er mine eyes beheld, and if thou wilt join my service I will clothe thee with a better coat than that thou hast upon thy back; thou shalt eat and drink of the best, and at every Christmas-tide fourscore marks shall be thy wage. I trow thou drawest better bow than that same coward knave, Robin Hood, that dared not show his face here this day. Say, good fellow, wilt thou join my service?"

"Nay, that will I not," quoth the stranger, roughly. "I will be mine own, and no man in all merry England shall be my master."

"Then get thee gone, and a murrain[18] seize thee!" cried the Sheriff, and his voice trembled with anger. "And by my faith and troth[19] I have a good part of a mind to have thee beaten for thine insolence!" Then he turned upon his heel and strode away.

It was a right motley company that gathered about the noble greenwood tree in Sherwood's depths that same day. A score and more of barefoot friars were there, and some that looked like tinkers, and some that seemed to be sturdy beggars and rustic hinds[20]; and seated upon a mossy couch was one all clad in tattered scarlet, with a patch over one eye; and in his hand he held the golden arrow that was the prize of the great shooting-match. Then, amidst a noise of talking and laughter, he took the patch from off his eye and stripped away the scarlet rags from off his body and

---

18. Murrain means disease or plague.
19. Troth means promise.
20. Hind is a term for farmworker or servant.

showed himself all clothed in fair Lincoln green, and quoth he: "Easy come these things away, but walnut stain cometh not so speedily from yellow hair." Then all laughed louder than before, for it was Robin Hood himself that had won the prize from the Sheriff's very hands.

Then all sat down to the woodland feast and talked amongst themselves of the merry jest that had been played upon the Sheriff, and of the adventures that had befallen each member of the band in his disguise. But when the feast was done, Robin Hood took Little John apart and said, "Truly am I vexed in my blood, for I heard the Sheriff say today, 'Thou shootest better than that coward knave, Robin Hood, that dared not show his face here this day.' I would fain let him know who it was who won the golden arrow from out his hand, and also that I am no coward such as he takes me to be."

Then Little John said, "Good master, take thou me and Will Stutely and we will send yon fat Sheriff news of all this by a messenger such as he doth not expect."

That day the Sheriff sat at meat in the great hall of his house at Nottingham Town. Long tables stood down the hall, at which sat men-at-arms and household servants and good stout villains,[21] in all fourscore and more. There they talked of the day's shooting as they ate their meat and quaffed their ale. The Sheriff sat at the head of the table upon a raised seat under a canopy, and beside him sat his dame.

"By my troth," said he, "I did reckon full roundly that that knave, Robin Hood, would be at the game today. I did not think that he was such a coward. But who could that saucy knave be who answered me to my beard so bravely? I wonder that I did not have him beaten; but there was something about him that spoke of other things than rags and tatters."

Then, even as he finished speaking, something fell rattling among the dishes on the table, while those that sat near started up wondering what it might be. After a while one of the men-at-arms gathered courage enough to pick it up and bring it to the Sheriff. Then every one saw that it was a blunted gray goose shaft, with a fine scroll, about the thickness of a goose quill, tied near to its head. The Sheriff opened the scroll and glanced at it, while the veins upon his forehead swelled and his cheeks grew ruddy with rage as he read, for this was what he saw:—

"Now Heaven bless thy grace this day
Say all in sweet Sherwood,
For thou didst give the prize away
To merry Robin Hood."

You can follow Robin Hood's many other adventures in the book from which this tale is taken. You might also want to read another version, *The Chronicles of Robin Hood* by Rosemary Sutcliff. Or, for a different view of life in long-ago England, try *The Boy's King Arthur* by Sidney Lanier.

---

21. A villain (or villein) is a half-free peasant—one who is under the control of his lord but has the rights of a free man when dealing with others.

This Is My Rock
by David McCord

This is my rock
And here I run
To steal the secret of the sun;

This is my rock
And here come I
Before the night has swept the sky;

This is my rock,
This is the place
I meet the evening face to face.

Afternoon on a Hill
by Edna St. Vincent Millay

I will be the gladdest thing
   Under the sun!
I will touch a hundred flowers
   And not pick one.

I will look at cliffs and clouds
   With quiet eyes,
Watch the wind bow down the grass,
   And the grass rise.

And when lights begin to show
   Up from the town,
I will mark which must be mine,
   And then start down!

Pippa's Song
by Robert Browning

The year's at the spring
And day's at the morn;
Morning's at seven;
The hillside's dew-pearled;
The lark's on the wing;
The snail's on the thorn:
God's in His heaven—
All's right with the world!

A Word
by Emily Dickinson

A word is dead
When it is said,
    Some say.

I say it just
Begins to live
    That day.

Certainty
by Emily Dickinson

I never saw a moor,
I never saw the sea;
Yet know I how the heather looks,
And what a wave must be.

I never spoke with God,
Nor visited in heaven;
Yet certain am I of the spot
As if the chart were given.

Follow the Gleam
by Alfred, Lord Tennyson

Not of the sunlight,   Launch your vessel,
Not of the moonlight,   And crowd your canvas,
Not of the starlight!   And ere it vanishes
O young Mariner,   Over the margin,
Down to the haven,   After it, follow it,
Call your companions,   Follow The Gleam.

The Prayer of the Little Bird
by Carmen Bernos de Gasztold
translated by Rumer Godden

Dear God,
I don't know how to pray by myself
very well,
but will You please
protect my little nest from wind and rain?
Put a great deal of dew on the flowers,
many seeds in my way.
Make Your blue very high,
Your branches lissom;
let Your kind light stay late in the sky
and set my heart brimming with such music
that I must sing, sing, sing....
Please, Lord.

If I Can Stop One Heart from Breaking
by Emily Dickinson

If I can stop one heart from breaking
I shall not live in vain,
If I can ease one life the aching
Or cool one pain,
Or help one fainting robin
Unto his nest again,
I shall not live in vain.

Others
by Harry Behn

Even though it's raining
I don't wish it wouldn't.
That would be like saying
I think it shouldn't.
I'd rather be out playing
Than sitting hours and hours
Watching rain falling
In drips and drops and showers,
But what about the robins?
What about the flowers?

Dreams
by Langston Hughes

Hold fast to dreams
For if dreams die
Life is a broken-winged bird
That cannot fly.

Hold fast to dreams
For when dreams go
Life is a barren field
Frozen with snow.

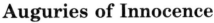

Auguries of Innocence
by William Blake

To see a World in a grain of sand,
And a Heaven in a wild flower,
Hold Infinity in the palm of your hand,
And Eternity in an hour.

To Dark Eyes Dreaming
by Zilpha Keatley Snyder

Dreams go fast and far
   these days.
They go by rocket thrust.
They go arrayed
   in lights
     or in the dust of stars.
Dreams, these days,
   go fast and far.
Dreams are young, these days,
   or very old,
They can be black
   or blue or gold.
They need no special charts,
   nor any fuel.
It seems, only one rule applies,
   to all our dreams—
They will not fly except in open sky.
   A fenced-in dream
     will die.

(Acknowledgments continued from page 2)
1962 by Elizabeth Coatsworth Beston. Reprinted by permission of Macmillan Publishing Company. "The Storm" excerpted from Hills End by Ivan Southall. Copyright © 1962 by Ivan Southall. Reprinted with permission of Macmillan Publishing Company, and Angus and Robertson, Publishers.

Macmillan of Canada: "The Difficulty of Living on Other Planets" and "There Was a Man" from Nicholas Knock and Other People by Dennis Lee. Copyright © 1974 by Dennis Lee. Reprinted by permission of Macmillan of Canada, A Division of Canada Publishing Corp.

Mike Makley: "The New Kid" by Mike Makley. Copyright © 1975 by Mike Makley. By permission of the author.

Norma Millay: "Afternoon on a Hill" from Collected Poems by Edna St. Vincent Millay, published by Harper & Row. Copyright 1917, 1945 by Edna St. Vincent Millay.

William Morrow & Company, Inc.: "The Knockout" and "The Sidewalk Racer" from The Sidewalk Racer and Other Poems of Sports and Motion by Lillian Morrison. Copyright © 1977 by Lillian Morrison. By permission of Lothrop, Lee & Shepard Books (A Division of William Morrow & Co.). "Bees" and "The Hummingbird" from Zoo Doings by Jack Prelutsky. Copyright © 1970, 1983 by Jack Prelutsky. By permission of Greenwillow Books (A Division of William Morrow & Company, Inc.). "The Lion" from Zoo Doings by Jack Prelutsky. Copyright © 1974, 1983 by Jack Prelutsky. By permission of Greenwillow Books (A Division of William Morrow & Company, Inc.). "The Troll" from Nightmares by Jack Prelutsky. Copyright © 1976 by Jack Prelutsky. By permission of Greenwillow Books (A Division of William Morrow & Company). Published in the UK by A & C Black Ltd., 1978.

John Murray Ltd.: "Under the willow—" from Autumn Wind, Wisdom of the East Series translated by Lewis Mackenzie. Published by John Murray Ltd.

Hugh Noyes for Alfred Noyes Literary Estate: "The Highwayman" from Collected Poems: Volume One by Alfred Noyes. Copyright 1913, 1941.

Oxford University Press: "The sunrise tints the dew" and "In spite of chills and cold" from A Year of Japanese Epigrams translated by William Porter (1911). Used by permission of Oxford University Press.

Prentice-Hall, Inc.: "Wanted—A Witch's Cat" from What Witches Do by Shelagh McGee. Copyright © 1980 by Felix Gluck Press, Ltd. Published by Prentice-Hall, Inc., Englewood Cliffs, NJ 07632. Reprinted by permission of Prentice-Hall, Inc., Felix Gluck Press, Ltd., and the author.

Random House, Inc.: "The Wolf" by Georgia Roberts Durston. "The Lizard" from A Child's Bestiary by John Gardner. Copyright © 1977 by John Gardner and Boskydell Artists Ltd. Reprinted by permission of Alfred A. Knopf, Inc., and Georges Borchardt, Inc. "Dreams" from The Dream Keeper and Other Poems by Langston Hughes. Copyright 1932 by Alfred A. Knopf, Inc. and renewed 1960 by Langston Hughes. Reprinted by permission of Alfred A. Knopf, Inc.

Scholastic Inc.: "Wind-Wolves" by William D. Sargent from the Scholastic Writing Awards Program. Copyright © 1926 by Scholastic Inc. Reprinted by permission of Scholastic Inc.

The San Francisco Examiner: "Casey at the Bat" by Ernest L. Thayer.

Lloyd Sarett Stockdale: "Wolf Cry" from Many Many Moons by Lew Sarett, copyright 1948 by Lew Sarett. Used by permission of Lloyd Sarett Stockdale.

Margaret Winsor Stubbs: "This Little Pig Built a Spaceship" (text only) from The Space Child's Mother Goose, text by Frederick Winsor; illustrations by Marian Perry. Copyright © 1958. Published by Simon & Schuster.

Yoshiko Uchida: "The Old Man with the Bump" from The Dancing Kettle and Other Japanese Folk Tales by Yoshiko Uchida. Copyright 1949, 1977 by Yoshiko Uchida. Reprinted by permission of the author.

United Educators, Inc.: "Far across hill and dale" and "I came to look, and lo." My Book House, © United Educators, Inc. Reprinted by permission.

Viking Penguin Inc.: "The Prayer of the Little Bird" from Prayers from the Ark by Carmen Bernos de Gasztold, translated by Rumer Godden. Copyright 1947, 1955 by Editions du Cloitre. English text copyright © 1962 by Rumer Godden. Reprinted by permission of Viking Penguin Inc., and Curtis Brown Group Ltd.—London.

Wesleyan University Press: "The Base Stealer" from The Orb Weaver by Robert Francis. Copyright 1960 by Robert Francis. Used by permission of Wesleyan University Press.

Xerox Education Publications: "Foul Shot" by Edwin A. Hoey, reprinted by permission of Read magazine, published by Xerox Education Publications. Copyright © 1962, Xerox Corp.

Illustration acknowledgments

The publishers of *Childcraft* gratefully acknowledge the courtesy of the following photographers, agencies, and organizations for illustrations in this volume. When all the illustrations for a sequence of pages are from a single source, the inclusive page numbers are given. In all other instances, the page numbers refer to facing pages, which are considered as a single unit or spread. All illustrations are the exclusive property of the publishers of *Childcraft* unless names are marked with an asterisk (*).

6–21: Elizabeth Miles	108–113: Marlene Ekman	198–201: Lynd Ward
22: Betsy Day	114–117: Sue Rother	203–211: Jim Pearson
24–30: Jennifer Emry-Perrott	119: Susan Stamato	212–217: David Wenzel
32–37: Rodney Pate	121–127: Elise Primavera	218–229: Cheryl Arnemenin
38–41: Betsy Day	128–130: David Wenzel	230–231: Mou-sien Tseng
42–45: Louise Fitzhugh*	131–140: Steven Clay	232–242: Jim Pearson
58–65: Mou-sien Tseng	145–151: Bert Dodson	245: Marlene Ekman
66–69: Marlene Ekman	152–153: Mou-sien Tseng	246–262: Bert Dodson
70–81: John Dawson	154–162: Robert Baxter	265: Koko Fukazawa
83–85: Bert Dodson	165–172: Bradley Clark	267–276: Floyd Cooper
87: Marlene Ekman	174–175: Susan Stamato	279–294: Hal Frenck
89–91: Jerry Pinkney	176–186: Robert Korta	296–299: Mou-sien Tseng
93–99: Mou-sien Tseng	188–194: Arvis Stewart	
100–107: Susan Stamato	196: Edward Gorey*	Cover: Yoshi Miyake

Author Index

This index is divided into two parts: **Authors of Stories** and **Authors of Poems.** If you know the name of the author you are looking for, use this index. You can also find a story or a poem by using the **Title Index** or a poem by using the **First-Line Index.** For more stories and poems, see the indexes in volumes 1 and 2. For stories and poems in all other volumes, see the entries **poems and rhymes, poets,** and **stories** in the General Index in Volume 15.

Authors of Stories

Andersen, Hans Christian
  Emperor's New Clothes, The, 100
Armstrong, William H.
  Homecoming, The, 188
Benson, Sally
  Flight of Icarus, The, 208
  Theseus and the Minotaur, 202
Carey, Bonnie
  Baba Yaga's Geese, 114
Cober, Mary E.
  How It Snowed Fur and Rained Fry Cakes in Western Virginia, 199
Courlander, Harold
  Cow-Tail Switch, The, 32
Fillmore, Parker
  Clever Manka, 120
Fitzhugh, Louise
  Harriet's Secret, 42
George, Jean Craighead
  Nina Terrance, 131

Grahame, Kenneth
  Toad's Escape, 6
Grimm, Jakob and Wilhelm
  Bremen Town Musicians, The, 88
Herzog, George
  Cow-Tail Switch, The, 32
Hill, Kay
  Glooscap and His People, 143
Kendall, Carol
  Living Kuan-yin, The, 93
Le Guin, Ursula K.
  Boy Who Became a Wizard, The, 176
Li, Yao-wen
  Living Kuan-yin, The, 93
Mowat, Farley
  I Find Wol, 24
O'Dell, Scott
  I Leave the Island, 164
Parker, K. Langloh
  Why the Kangaroo Hops on Two Legs, 83

Pyle, Howard
  Shooting-Match at Nottingham Town, The, 279
Sherlock, Philip M.
  Anansi and the Plantains, 108
Sneve, Virginia Driving Hawk
  Thunder Butte, 70
Southall, Ivan
  Storm, The, 218
Speare, Elizabeth George
  Stranger in the Land, A, 232
Stevenson, Robert Louis
  I Strike the Jolly Roger, 246
Uchida, Yoshiko
  Old Man with the Bump, The, 58
Walsh, Jill Paton
  New Way, A, 154
Yep, Laurence
  Challenge, The, 267

Authors of Poems

Armour, Richard
  Good Sportsmanship, 67
Bashō
  haiku, 264
Behn, Harry
  Others, 298
Bernos de Gásztold, Carmen
  Prayer of the Little Bird, The, 298
Blake, William
  Auguries of Innocence, 299
Boncho
  haiku, 265
Brady, June
  Far Trek, 174
Browning, Robert
  Home Thoughts from Abroad, 231
  Pippa's Song, 297
Carman, Bliss
  Vagabond Song, A, 230
Carroll, Lewis
  Jabberwocky, 187

Chipp, Elinor
  Wild Geese, 230
Chiyo
  haiku, 265
Chora
  haiku, 264
Coatsworth, Elizabeth
  Swift Things Are Beautiful, 245
Cole, William
  Back Yard, July Night, 175
  Bananananananananana, 87
Dickinson, Emily
  Bird, A, 23
  Certainty, 297
  If I Can Stop One Heart From Breaking, 298
  Word, A, 297
Durston, Georgia Roberts
  Wolf, The, 153
Eliot, T. S.
  Macavity: The Mystery Cat, 196

Francis, Robert
  Base Stealer, The, 67
Gardner, John
  Lizard, The, 119
Garland, Hamlin
  Do You Fear the Wind?, 152
Grahame, Kenneth
  Toad's Song, 22
Hoey, Edwin A.
  Foul Shot, 68
Hovey, Richard
  Sea Gypsy, The, 231
Hughes, Langston
  Dreams, 299
Issa
  haiku, 265
Jōsa
  haiku, 264
Kennedy, X. J.
  Nineteenth-Moon-of-Neptune Beasts, The, 174
Kikuriō
  haiku, 264

Title Index

This index is divided into two parts: **Titles of Stories** and **Titles of Poems.** If you know the title of the story or poem you are looking for, use this index. You can also find a story or a poem by using the **Author Index** or a poem by using the **First-Line Index.** For more stories and poems, see the indexes in volumes 1 and 2. For stories and poems in all other volumes, see the entries **poems and rhymes, poets,** and **stories** in the General Index in Volume 15.

Titles of Stories

Titles of Poems

First-Line Index to Poems

Use this index to find a poem if you know only the first line of the poem. You can also find a poem by using the **Author Index** or the **Title Index.** For more poems, see the indexes in volumes 1 and 2. For poems in all other volumes, see the entries **poems and rhymes** and **poets** in the General Index in Volume 15.